170-14
£27.00

SUCCESSFUL MINERAL COLLECTING AND PROSPECTING

Books by Richard M. Pearl

Successful Mineral Collecting and Prospecting
How to Know the Minerals and Rocks
Colorado Gem Trails
Mineral Collectors Handbook
America's Mountain: Pikes Peak and the Pikes Peak Region
Nature as Sculptor: A Geologic Interpretation of Colorado Scenery
Colorado Gem Trails and Mineral Guide
Geology: Physical and Historical
Rocks and Minerals
Popular Gemology
Questions Answered About the Mineral Kingdom
Guide to Geologic Literature

With Dr. H. C. Dake
The Art of Gem Cutting

Successful Mineral Collecting and Prospecting

By RICHARD M. PEARL

Department of Geology
Colorado College, Colorado Springs, Colorado

BONANZA BOOKS · NEW YORK

SUCCESSFUL MINERAL COLLECTING AND PROSPECTING

Contents

To Harvey and Addie Nininger
America's pioneer prospectors and collectors
of meteorites

Preface

This well-illustrated book is the first book of general distribution that combines the related interests of prospectors and hobbyists in the worldwide search for minerals.

The prospector, although primarily concerned with commercial deposits that can be mined, sold, or leased, need not neglect material of specimen value. In fact, specimens, especially from a marginal or unproductive deposit, can often be disposed of more readily, as well as more profitably, to mineral collectors than in the usual mineral market. Many a mining family shows with pride the attractive crystals or ores obtained during past years, and in turn is a likely source of specimens for the visiting collector.

The mineral collector probably does not live who would ignore a discovery that could be transformed into a producing mine or quarry, even though his original intention was only to enjoy recreation in the outdoors and bring back something from a weekend or vacation to increase his private exhibit at home. Unexpected success may convert the collector-hobbyist into a prospector; the interests of the two groups, if not their manner of approach, are much alike.

To help both prospector and mineral collector, this book has been written. It describes the importance of the mineral industries to civilization and relates the history of their development. It tells what minerals are of most importance, and hence most worth looking for, emphasizing the changes that have taken place since the time when gold was almost the only mineral sought. It makes clear, however, that the era of the foot prospector is not over. On the contrary, his opportunities have enlarged vastly, so that they now include not only the precious metals, but a host of other substances as well. We are fast reaching the day when every earth material will be of value; the horizons of the prospector are expanding at the same rate.

This book describes fully the equipment used in prospecting for minerals—including the radioactive ores—and the methods employed in the highly personal art of mineral finding. The recognition and identification of minerals is explained, along with directions on securing an assay or analysis, and staking a mining claim of either vein or placer type. Testing minerals at home by various simple means is discussed, together with information about ways to start and improve a mineral collection. Separate chapters are devoted to the science and hobby of gemology—the study of precious stones—and to the abundant and popular quartz minerals and rocks. As a guide to prospecting and collecting in the United States, a summary is given of the principal mineral resources of each of the fifty states. Magazines and a selected list of books are recommended for further reading and continued study.

I must express my deep appreciation for the generous and effective cooperation of Elizabeth Shafer; Raymond C. Colwell, formerly of the U. S. Forest Service; Dr. Evan J. Scott, associated with the University of Colorado and Colorado College; Eleanor Steiner; Bessie Vermillion; Verna W. Alair; and my wife, Mignon W. Pearl. The drawings are the work of Mrs. Pearl and Jeanette Maas. Reo N. Pickens, Jr., took the color photographs.

Richard M. Pearl
Colorado College

Chapter 1

THE SEARCH FOR
MINERAL WEALTH

Chapter 1

THE SEARCH FOR MINERAL WEALTH

tor, from the Old and New Stone
down to the present day, has made
to almost every material advance
Through his persistent search for
, we have safer, more comfortable,
shelter, more efficient means of
tter lighting. Our diet has been
have at our disposal most of the
und in the average home, from
he multiplicity of gadgets used in
basement workshop, and the fam-
have more varied resources for
ding improved sports equipment,
tertainment of motion pictures,
ion. We have a simple and work-
xchange which will—provided
h of it!—purchase most of these
more reliable ways of defending
sickness, because of the enter-
ector, we may, in certain ill-
n more dependable medical

lector, though regarded as a
same time a true prospector.
ing out to find a choice speci-
would not suddenly acquire a
ding uranium or some other
erial and want to stake his
s good fortune to a successful
re is little real difference be-
r and the mineral collector,
uired to tip the balance be-
eover, the mineral collector
self a prospector and should
during intervals of outdoor

pleasure, contribute much in the vastly needful
search for mineral wealth.

The Birth of Prospecting

Men of the two Stone Ages probably became
prospectors more by accident than by design. They
were first of all concerned with recovering materials that might be useful as implements and weapons. Except for ornamentation, they were less interested in the mineral content of rocks than in
their usefulness in furnishing the necessities of life
and in providing defense. The splinter of bone
used as an awl suddenly broke or eventually crum-
bled. The gnarled branch that served as a club
split under the force of a delivered blow, or weathered and rotted. In flint, composed of silica like
that of quartz, this early ancestor of ours found a
substance better adapted to his needs. Its sharp-
edged flakes served as scrapers and knives. Larger,
rounded stones served as hammers. And as man
learned to shape flint and to fasten it with thongs
to wooden hafts and shafts, he created the arrow
and the war hammer. With the working of the
flint deposits found in ledges of soft limestone, with
the shaping of its shards and nodules into weapons, primitive man engaged in his first manufacturing venture.

As the need for more practicable weapons and
tools led man to the use of flint, so did his gradual
abandonment of a diet of uncooked flesh, berries,
and nuts in favor of cereals and of meat—roasted
or seethed—send him in search of salt deposits.
The demand for this seasoning determined the direction of trade routes toward ancient Palmyra,

11

the Libyan Desert, the Dnieper estuary, and India.

Primordial man, however, was as little limited in his use of minerals by his genuine need for implements, weapons, and a palatable diet as is his modern counterpart. He succumbed quite naturally to the brightness of nuggets of gold, silver, and copper, and to the odd patterns and vivid

U. S. Geological Survey

These two primitive stone tools were found at the old turquoise mines at Cerillos, near Sante Fe, New Mexico. They were used by the Indians who worked these, the oldest gem mines in the Western Hemisphere.

colorings of gem stones. These he very largely utilized either for personal adornment or as amulets —charms to bring good luck or to ward off evil. Early French explorers venturing into the land of Hiawatha reported that the Indians venerated bits of shiny native copper picked up from stream beds or outcrops as gods or as the gifts of tribal deities. Other travelers of the Age of Exploration gave accounts of the natives of the Guinea Coast and of the Malay Peninsula wearing rings and bracelets of gold or silver, and of the use of such metals as symbols of rank and authority by tribal leaders.

Although gold (its allure has never faded!) was probably the first metal to attract man, copper minerals seem to have been the first to have been mined extensively. Copper may have been obtained by the Egyptians in the Sinai Peninsula as early as 5000 B.C. The discovery that copper, when fused with tin at high temperatures, produces bronze has not, however, been credited to them. Implements and utensils of a rudimentary bronze have been found among the ruins of an older city on the site of Troy, this more ancient city belong-

ing possibly to the period between 2500 and 2000 B.C. In the region of the lower Danube, bronze appears to have come into use at about this same time. There, the discovery of the making of bronze may have been facilitated by the fact that the copper ore contained a fair proportion of tin.

It is easy for most of us to imagine a dramatic moment in history when the Bronze Age succeeded the last Stone Age—the moment when one of our early ancestors presumably lifted from among the ashes of a fire a lump of metal considerably less malleable than the pure copper with which he supposed he was working. The chances are that he regarded his new find with some consternation, that he only very gradually discovered its possibilities in terms of tools, household wares, and weapons, and that his understanding and systematizing of the process of making alloys was something painfully achieved. It has been suggested that this step alone, beginning by coincidence, may have occupied a millennium.

We owe to the poets of classic Greece our notion of four successive cultural ages of the world: the Age of Gold (the era of the gods); the Age of Silver (the time of the first men); the Age of Bronze (the time of heroes); and the Age of Iron (the period of man's decadence and ultimate destruction). But if geologic finds are correct, it was not in that area of the eastern Mediterranean that iron was first used. Nor was it in Egypt, though rich deposits of iron ore existed side by side with the copper beds of the Sinai Peninsula. Some time during the 13th Century B.C., the Hittites, who lived in the mountains and on the plateaus of Asia Minor, are believed to have made the first use of iron. All evidence at present points to the fact, however, that this early iron was of meteoritic origin and had not been taken from the earth as ore. Hence the swords of the heroes of ancient epic may literally be said, as the warriors themselves claimed, to have been gifts from heaven. Lacking a completely adequate smelting process, these early workers in iron were able to remove only a portion of its impurities by melting the metal, and were able to produce a serviceable material only by repeatedly heating and hammering the spongy iron. Imperfect though this early smelting method certainly was, it proved capable of being applied to the extracting of metal from a number of simple high-grade ores. Thus, through this toilsome means, the ancient world was able to put to use in larger volume its resources in iron, lead, zinc, tin, and mercury, as well as gold, silver, and copper.

Discovery of the New World

While we are, in a real sense, still living in the Iron Age, we cannot pass immediately to the effect upon prospecting caused by the Industrial Revolution of the 18th Century and later without first mentioning the tremendous impetus given to the search for precious metals and gems by the discovery of the wealth of the New World. Columbus made his first voyage, ending in the unwitting discovery of vast lands, as much to find riches in gold, pearls, and spices as to substantiate an old theory as to the shape of the earth. Had this not been so, it is doubtful whether he would have been able to interest the rulers of Spain in his venture at all. The bits of alluvial gold which the natives of Guanahani and Haiti brought to him and his men convinced them of the presence of valuable deposits of the metal, and led others to the ruthless driving of native and imported slave labor to extract

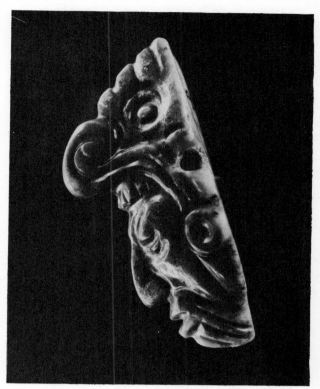

Middle American Research Institute

Exceptional craftsmanship is shown in this hard-stone carving of a Mayan head pendant from Yucatan, Mexico. The material is jadeite, the more valuable of the two kinds of true jade.

Middle American Research Institute

Owing to its extremely sharp cutting edge, obsidian—a natural glass of volcanic origin—was used by early man for weapons and implements. These Aztec blades were found in Mexico.

all the precious metal possible from the lands of the Western Hemisphere. Of that brilliant and cruel epoch, only the romantic flavor remains.

The inhabitants of the Americas at the time of Spanish colonization were in a primitive stage of development in their use of metals. They appreciated gold and silver principally for decorative uses. Stories were told to the Spaniards of a king whose entire body was gilded anew with powdered gold each morning. Yet, in some places, natives were beginning to use copper, and sometimes more precious metals, for tools and weapons. Farther to the north, in the territories that were to be occupied somewhat later by the English and the French, metal culture was in a stage no more advanced: copper was used in various kinds of body ornamentation; meteoritic iron was hammered into blades for cutting. Because the northern Indian braves arrayed themselves in paint, they also mined iron ocher and manganese oxide with which to make the red and black colors they particularly favored. Nevertheless, it was the wealth of Mexico and South and Central America—wealth amassed through the efforts of unknown prospectors and miners among the Aztecs and the Incas and plundered by the conquistadors—that helped to shape modern Europe and to give birth to high hopes among the British that the planting of a colony in Virginia would lead to similar discoveries of stores of precious metals.

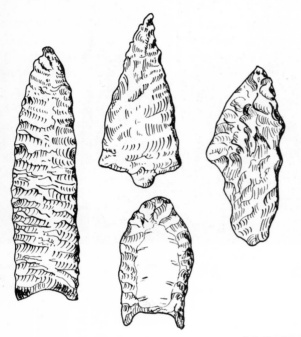

H. M. Wormington

American Indian arrowheads of flint and related minerals differ according to the culture responsible for them. These four distinctive designs are characterized as Oblique Yuma, Sandia, Folsom, and Gypsum Cave, all of western United States origin.

The Industrial Revolution

With the beginnings of the Industrial Revolution in the 18th Century, prospecting became a full-time business in itself, centering particularly in the search for coal and iron—early manufacturing's two basic needs—and extending in the two centuries following to a large number of metals, nonmetallic minerals and rocks, and fuels. Hardly anyone needs to be reminded of the degree to which our economy and its prosperity are dependent upon the discovery and development of our natural resources—hence ultimately upon the activities of the prospector. Most of the changes that have occurred in our civilization since the turn of the 19th Century have come through our increased use of natural resources. Indeed, many economic historians take the view that our attitudes and ideas change largely as the physical bases of our lives are modified.

The first of the two great resources to modify life in the Western world of the 18th Century was coal. It was used to smelt the ore to obtain the metal to make the machinery. Then it was used to generate the power to put the machinery in motion. Known to the Greeks and Romans but little used by them except in some areas for heating purposes, utilized by the Chinese at an early time both for heating purposes and for the "firing" of their porcelain, used in Britain by its Roman conquerors to heat the baths at Uriconium and Aquae Solis, coal never really came into its own until there was need for a source of mechanical power. The genius of Newcomen and Watt in the 1700's produced the stationary steam engine; and the work of Trevithick, Blenkinsop, and Stephenson in the early 1800's harnessed steam to locomotion. That these developments took place in the British Isles was not altogether a coincidence. England and southern Scotland were incalculably rich in coal, the energy-producing mineral vital to steam. Because their resources seemed inexhaustible, the British were able not only to meet all their own coal requirements, but also to export coal to the countries of western Europe, the Far East, and the United States. Late in the 19th Century, severe competition in coal production came from the United States and Germany, competition that ultimately deprived Britain of its position as the industrial leader of the world. Shortly after the beginning of our own century, the world was estimated to hold coal reserves that would last, at the

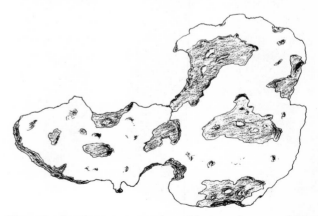

Nuggets of native copper, such as this, were hammered into useful and ornamental objects long before the Bronze Age. The Upper Peninsula of Michigan is the world's greatest source of copper in its pure state.

rate they were then being taken from the ground, for about 3,000 years.

The extent to which these resources of coal will be affected by the development of other sources of heat and energy cannot as yet be determined. A most significant thing to note in this changed situation is the role that the prospector has played in it. For it is he, often armed with a geologist's knowledge, who has tapped our present resources in oil, natural gas, and uranium and other radioactive substances that will eventually give us heat and power. And it is he, working hand in hand with the laboratory scientist, who will contribute in future times to the development of other sources of energy from materials perhaps now regarded as worthless—as in the past, coal once was.

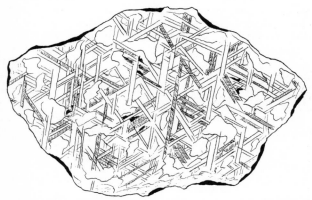

H. H. Nininger

When a metallic meteorite is sawed open, polished, and etched with acid, its crystalline structure is revealed. Each "fall" is different. This is the Tonganoxie, Kansas, meteorite.

As we have already mentioned, iron, the second basic material of the Industrial Revolution, was used by early man in its meteoritic form. Then, as in later times, the nations that possessed iron and used it in weapons were the conquerors and empire-builders. But the methods of working such iron were arduous as well as exceedingly slow, and the product, by modern standards, would be thought inferior. Indeed, it was not until the 14th Century A.D. that a blower was devised that would raise the temperature of the furnace high enough to make cast iron. Much of this early cast iron went into the making of cannon and cannon balls. An appreciation of the possibilities of coal as a smelting fuel, and the perfecting of a coking process early in the 1700's (a development rendered particularly urgent because of the steady depletion of forests in the making of charcoal, the

former smelting fuel), at last placed coal at the service of iron, which could then be produced in sufficient quantity to be used industrially. With the invention in the 1850's by Bessemer of his process for making steel, the story of iron comes to a pause.

To the story of any metal there is no real terminus, for what appears useless today may be of supreme importance tomorrow. Likewise, what appears of the greatest value today may find itself among strong rivals tomorrow—as steel is now rivaled by concrete as a construction material. It is not amiss here, incidentally, to point out that the constituents of concrete, which are cement (from limestone) and stone aggregate, are other contributions of the prospector. In fact, the finding of a suitable bed of common sand near a large city may be a more profitable discovery than a gold mine.

The history of the development of our natural resources following the beginning of the Industrial Revolution is one in which, unfortunately, there are many chapters devoted to greed in their acquisition and criminal heedlessness in their waste. The fuel and other mineral materials uncovered through the energy and perseverance of the prospector have too often been exploited without prudence or conscience, squandered in peace and wasted in war.

Another ore of lead is pyromorphite. The crystal is from Pennsylvania.

The Atomic Age

As the Industrial Revolution touched off a worldwide search for coal and iron and other raw materials, so has the Atomic Age set off a global search for uranium and thorium, the radioactive ores.

Known as early as 1789 when it was identified by the German chemist Klaproth, and first used as a coloring agent for pottery, uranium was not utilized for its fissionable properties until World

War II. At that time, locations of adequate supplies of this metal were not known. Through the enterprise of private prospectors, as well as of geologists in the employ of their governments, deposits have been uncovered in the region of Great Bear Lake in northwest Canada, on the Colorado Plateau, in the Congo, and in Australia, Czechoslovakia, and Portugal.

Thorium is of more recent date. Isolated in 1828 by the Swedish chemist Berzelius, it has been in familiar use only for the past seventy-five years. Thorium, coming mostly from the minerals called monazite and thorite, has been found in various parts of the United States, in Brazil, India and southeastern Asia, Australia, and South Africa.

The remarkable fireproof substance known as asbestos is a natural mineral. It can be spun and woven like vegetable fibers. This specimen came from Orleans County, Vermont.

Galena is the most important ore of lead. It is a heavy, silvery-colored mineral with a bright luster.

Malachite and azurite are colorful ores of copper. The original crystals were blue azurite, but they have altered to green malachite. The locality is Tsumeb, South-West Africa.

Although not radioactive, beryllium is a metal of significance in the atomic-energy program. It is found in association with about fifty minerals and has been located in many of the same areas mentioned above and, in addition, in northern and northwestern Africa, Spain, and Portugal. The omission from this list of locations within the Soviet orbit (Czechoslovakia excepted) does not, as we know, mean that these minerals are not to be found there. All indications are to the contrary.

The temptation to think of prospecting principally in terms of uranium is great in these times, because of the urgent demand for this mineral as a defense material and as a source of benefits now only dreamed of, and also because a rich strike has

The first iron was obtained in the form of meteorites—the metallic remains of comets or of a shattered planet like the earth.

Bauxite, the only ore of aluminum, is readily recognized by its nodular growth. Arkansas is the principal source in the United States.

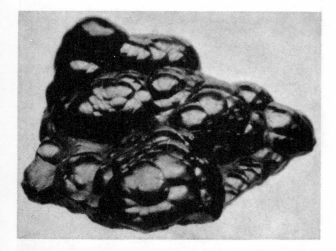

The most valuable ore of iron is hematite. It often has the botryoidal (grapelike) form shown by this specimen.

offered a quick road to wealth. The future prospector, however, needs to be reminded of the tremendous variety of mineral resources required by the industrial plants of any modern country. The comfort of modern man, his health and safety, and his material wealth depend very heavily, as we suggested at the outset, upon his discovery, energetic development, and intelligent use of the entire range of natural resources.

Metallic Minerals

Among the *metallic minerals* or *ores,* there are the precious ones—gold, silver, and platinum—and a gradually growing number of nonprecious ones: copper, lead, zinc, aluminum, chromium, molybdenum, nickel, lithium, mercury, cerium and related rare-earth metals, titanium, tungsten, manganese, tin, and iron—an unexhaustive enumeration.

It is estimated that the cream of the richest iron-bearing district in the United States, the Mesabi "range" at the head of Lake Superior, is good for only another generation or so at the present rate of consumption. The depletion of this district without the finding of new iron fields of equal size and grade could mean that our economy might soon tend to parallel that of Great Britain since 1900—increasingly depressed and unstable, dependent upon foreign sources for its most important metal.

Estimates on the available supply of uranium vary. We are told that world supplies may last a century, but one executive of a large uranium-mining company has stated that the United States has only a ten-year reserve of this essential material. The answer seems to depend upon the progress of civilian nuclear-power development.

The American prospector can enrich himself and help his country by opening up deposits of tin, chromium, platinum, columbium, and other metals relatively scarce within its borders.

Mineral Fuels

No one can be unaware of the importance of the *mineral fuels*—coal and petroleum—the two combustibles with which we presently power all but a very small percentage of our production and transportation. To these must be added natural gas. All three are referred to as "fossil fuels," because their energy has been stored in the earth for long geologic ages.

Gem Stones

Nor should the *gem stones* be passed by in the prospector's search for mineral wealth. Even though the richest area for gem prospecting in the United States lies in the West, other sections of the country have rewarded the prospector's patience and diligence, too. Tourmaline comes from Maine as well as California; a notable place for ruby is in North Carolina, where sapphire has also been found; silicified coral is taken from the coastal waters of Florida. Many states, especially Arkansas, have reported the occurrence of diamond. In the West, the range of gems to be found increases considerably. Jade of excellent quality comes from Wyoming and Alaska. Opal and turquoise are mined in Nevada. Agate, turquoise, and obsidian are taken from the placers and veins of Arizona. Sapphire, moss agate, and amethyst are typical of Montana. The list is apparently endless, and every state in the Union has a share, though in some cases a modest one.

Nonmetallic Minerals and Rocks

Finally, the rest of the *nonmetallic,* or *industrial, minerals and rocks,* of which there are hundreds, used in thousands of ways, may be found in some form within or near almost any community in the United States. Called nonmetallic because they are used without regard for the metal (iron or aluminum, for example) that may be part of their chemical formulas, these minerals include innumerable substances in daily use. They include the pigments used in paints; every kind of abrasive, from diamond to talc; materials used in the construction of thoroughfares and buildings from homes to schools, offices, and factories. Of the construction materials, space allows us to list only a few: granite, marble, sandstone, pumice, the gypsum used in plaster, the limestone used in cement, and asphalt. For ceramics, we mention potter's clay and feldspar. Among insulating and fire proofing materials, we may name asbestos, vermiculite, and perlite. In the group of nonmetallic

minerals used as fertilizers, there are phosphates, nitrates, and potash. The supply of any one of of them is not, with a growing population and an expanding economy, without limit. If our civilization is to continue at its present level, further sources of supply will have to be found, or substitutes provided.

The Prospector—
His Equipment and Methods

The modern prospector is in a position vastly improved over that of his predecessors in his quest for new sources of metals, mineral fuels, and nonmetallic minerals. Since the days when the pharaohs of Egypt gave commands that sent expeditions into the Sinai Peninsula, the Arabian Desert, and up the Nile Valley into the Sudan in search of copper, turquoise, and emerald, and since the time when Jason piloted the *Argo* between the Clashing Rocks on his voyage to seize the Golden Fleece (probably a raid on the gold-bearing regions of Georgia at the eastern foot of the Black Sea), even since the Spaniards plundered Mexico, Colombia, and Peru, the means at the disposal of the prospector in his search for mineral wealth have been greatly enlarged.

As we have already stated, at first and for many centuries the prospector fell into his role by accident. In the days before civilization, he came across gems, metals, other minerals, and rocks by chance and was content to use them pretty much

Alan M. Bateman

Medieval miners employing the divining rod.

as he found them, able to do little more than crudely reshape them. Generations of experience came slowly to the aid of these early prospectors, and they learned how to spot the more obvious evidences of mineral deposits lying close to the surface of the earth. The knowledge even of a large number of the prospectors who flocked to the Far West and Alaska in the 1850's and 1890's did not extend much beyond this.

In the Middle Ages, the prospector is said to have resorted to the use of the *divining rod* (now known also under the thought-teasing names of dowsing rod, doodlebug, and witch stick), counting upon it to respond to a magnetic pull in his hands to reveal the presence of ores buried more deeply. Although its medieval German inventor is reported to have been led to the gallows as a cheat and an impostor, and although present-day scientists almost to a man have discredited its use, many good folk still profess unlimited faith in the divining rod, especially in a search for hidden water sources.

Whereas the earliest prospectors probably limited their quests for gems and metals to outcrops, placering—the process of washing the sand and gravel of stream beds—is known to have come into use with the Egyptians as a mining technique at least as early as 4000 B.C. It was almost certainly used at that time by the prospector, too. The Golden Fleece purloined by Jason may, in the opinion of some authorities, have been a fleece used to line the sluice-box of a placer mine to catch the heavy metal as the water and sand poured through.

Prospecting has been systematized by the geologic staffs of the larger mining companies into effective means of locating desired ores. In areas that seem promising for certain kinds of metal, for example, a crew of trained geologists and their assistants may divide the region into parallel strips, working over each strip thoroughly, and taking samples from all rock outcrops.

Placering has likewise been systematized. In stream beds in which alluvial deposits of metal have been detected, a search party may work upstream, panning for the metal at frequent intervals. The stream, together with its branches or tributaries, is worked in this manner until particles of the mineral no longer show in the pan after washing. The order is then reversed. The party re-

Standard Oil Company, New Jersey

The gravimeter (or gravity meter) measures the varying pull of the earth according to the rock existing beneath the surface. In this way the kind and structure of rock can be determined. The site is near Crane, Texas.

The Fisher portable metal detector is widely used in prospecting as well as in treasure hunting.

traces its steps downstream, washing for the metal again at close intervals to find the spot at which it first appears in the stream bed. Here the search leaves the stream and moves up the slope. Miniature shafts are sunk, each one to the point where fragments of the mineral are seen. This process is repeated until at some point on the slope a shaft is sunk to bedrock without the appearance of these loose fragments, usually called *float*. Then the searchers trench between the last two pits, hoping to come in contact with the vein of ore.

Much of California's gold was taken by this method. A century ago, it would have been possible in the mountain ranges of California and Nevada (and somewhat later in the Rockies) to see the prospector, often alone, with his pick, shovel, gold pan, and supplies packed on a burro, drifting along the water courses of the high country. He explored the stream beds, the slopes dropping down toward them, and the rock ledges jutting above, stopping to pan the sediment accumulated in the middle reaches of a stream at the mouth of a canyon. Or he worked along a slope with his eye open for loose deposits of rust-stained quartz or the reddish, porous "iron hat," or *gossan,* that betrays the presence beneath of veins of possible silver- or gold-bearing sulfide ores. When the yearly onset of winter drove this lonely seeker from the hills, he descended into the desert to continue his efforts in the sands left by the seas or streams of long ago— there to be hampered by lack of water in the setting up of a true placer operation and usually also by the leanness of the mineralization. Yet, by these methods was much of the wealth of the United States discovered and taken from the ground during the years of the gold and silver fever of the 19th Century. Now, though most of the gold and silver placer deposits have been cleared of their riches, other metals—such as platinum, tin, and thorium—are being located and worked by the placer method.

In the search for subsurface deposits of commercially valuable ore, the medieval divining rod has been replaced by a number of more reliable instruments, from the *magnetic needle* used to indicate the presence of iron ore to the *Geiger counter* and *scintillation counter* used to identify radioactive minerals.

The Geiger counter, with its battery, its tube

containing a gas easily ionized by radioactive materials, and its electronic device for picking up and augmenting the electrical charges generated by the electrode within the tube of gas, is now a common item of equipment for the prospector and is not unknown to the sportsman.

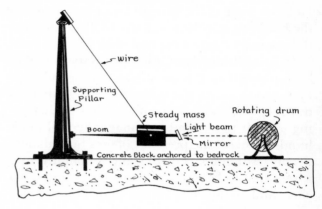

Gilluly, Waters, and Woodford

Natural earthquakes are recorded on seismographs such as this laboratory model. Portable seismographs are used in the field.

The *dip needle* and the more sensitive *magnetometer* work much as does a compass, the needle reacting to magnetic ores hidden in the earth. The *torsion balance* and *gravimeter* operate on the principle of gravitational attraction. Some minerals generate measureable currents of electricity as they react chemically to the moisture in the soil. The *seismograph,* an instrument used in the study of earthquakes, is also employed by the modern prospector. In an area where valuable minerals or oil deposits are suspected to be, a charge of explosives is detonated. The speed of the ground waves radiating from the center of the explosion is measured by a single seismograph, or more likely by a series of them placed at different distances. Rocks beneath the surface will transmit these waves faster than will soil. Other waves from the explosion deflected by rocks at depth also reveal valuable information to the prospector.

Lastly, we must not overlook the airplane and jeep as prospecting equipment. The jeep, with its four-wheel drive, will carry a man into rough country, along with his instruments and camping equipment. It is the burro of the modern prospector. And from a plane, as all air travelers know, more can be learned about the surface of the globe than the earth-bound might suppose. Outcrops which might not be come upon in weeks or months on the ground may be spotted and marked on maps for later investigation.

The Lures of Prospecting— Adventures and Bonanzas

In our review of the history of the use of mineral resources, and in our historical sketch of prospecting, we have spoken of it almost exclusively as a necessary preliminary to the business of mining on a commercial scale. Thousands of prospectors in all parts of the world and in all times have entered upon their search with the hope of "striking it rich," "finding a bonanza," "finding the mother lode," discovering gems of sufficient value or ores rich enough to lead to the founding of a private fortune. There have been other lures, however, and these have exerted their force upon more than one man who has taken to the geologist's hammer and gold pan. Some of the prospectors of the 19th-Century West cared less for the wealth they might discover than for the freedom they found in this way of living. The grubstake they accepted placed only a minor limitation upon this freedom. Off in the hills, no man was their master. Now, in the

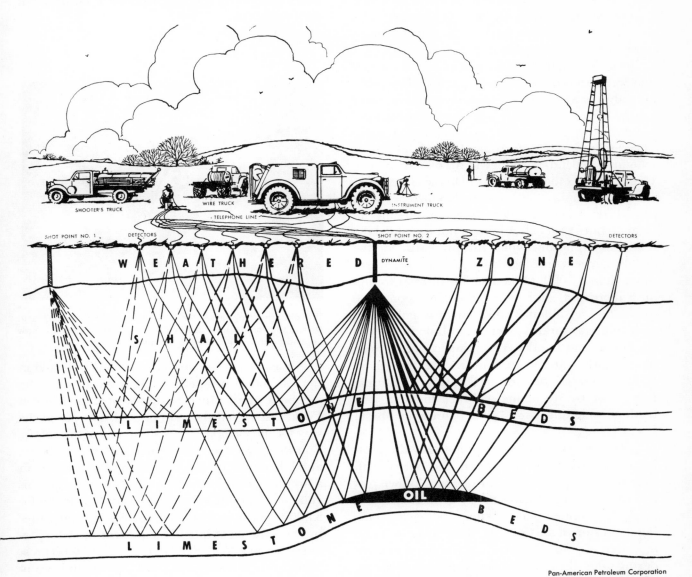

Pan-American Petroleum Corporation

Seismograph equipment is used in exploring for ores, petroleum, salt, sulfur, and other mineral resources.

West and in other likely sections of the country, the weekend prospector takes to the hills to see what he can see, to explore country new to him, to meet and talk with people living in the areas to be prospected, to prowl around the diggings of old mining settlements, and to add new specimens to rock collections. One can make of prospecting what he will. People in the area of Tampa Bay on the Florida Gulf Coast go to Ballast Point to collect coral. Texans keep an eye alert for specimens of topaz or agate. So it goes the world around. The chances are probably small that the amateur prospector will strike a bonanza, though this still happens occasionally, but he may count on seeing a lot of country and having a lot of pleasure. If he does not object to hard work, either, he may make some money at the same time.

Nevertheless, the stories of lucky breaks, of sudden fortunes large and small, persist; they probably always will, as long as hope remains in men's hearts. There is the story, for example, about a belated discovery in the Divine Gulch region of Eldorado County, California—the story of a man who found spending money in his own dooryard. Elisha Holmes took up land in Divine Gulch after the gold-rush days had passed into history, when the placer workings there were supposedly all cleaned out. Years after he had homesteaded the land, his grandson, while turning earth for the family garden, uncovered a gold nugget worth more than $1,000. Of course, his interest in digging increased, and before the afternoon wore away, he had about $1,500 worth of gold. Two gem hunters working over the rubble in the dry washes around Lander, Wyoming, collected some heavy, dark, water-worn boulders that turned out to be valuable jade, and a part-time California prospector by the name of Mack found a jade boulder weighing over 1,300 pounds in Shasta County.

Some fantastic stories credit not only the prospector but his beast of burden, the burro, with making strikes. Doubtless the one best known is of the white donkey furnished by grubstakers to a prospector named Noah Kellogg, who was scouring the region of the Coeur d'Alene River in Idaho in search of gold. His jack had the habit of wandering off in the night, and on one such occasion, after tracing him into a canyon and up a slope, Kellogg and a companion, Phil O'Rourke, found

the animal standing on an outcrop of ore, gazing mesmerized across the canyon at the opposite wall, where a body of exposed ore flashed in the morning sun. Thus were said to have been discovered both the Bunker Hill and Sullivan mines, prolific in lead and silver. A similar story is told of the discovery of the Tonopah mine in Nevada, a find of gold- and silver-bearing ores, this time located by a rancher, Jim Butler, whose burros had strayed during a dust storm and had taken shelter with impressive forethought in the lee of an outcrop of a dark rock. This rock assayed an average of $160 per ton, being part of a vein that over the years yielded its several owners a total of about $150,000,000.

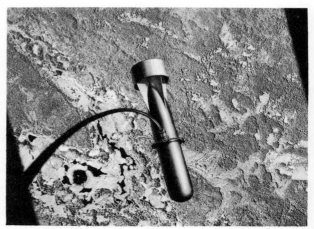

Aero Service Corporation

The airborne magnetometer is suspended from an airplane. Developed for wartime use in detecting submarines, it is now applied to finding hidden ore bodies.

All aspects of life are caught and reflected in stories about prospectors. Bob Womack, who owned a small ranch on the west slope of Pikes Peak, discovered the vein of gold that paved the way for the Cripple Creek stampede of the 1890's. Bob was never overly burdened with ranch chores, and killed time by digging around the premises in search of promising ore samples. He worked his gold vein as the El Paso mine and later sold it for $5,000. In contrast, a Colorado Springs carpenter by the name of Winfield Scott Stratton, who possessed some knowledge of geology and who prospected when trade was slack, also found ore of considerable value in the Cripple Creek region and staked his claims. Stratton went on to make

The helicopter has a tremendous future in the search for minerals. Canada is a leader in prospecting by aircraft, as seen here at Little Doctor Lake, Northwest Territories.

Socony Mobil Oil Company

millions, but Bob Womack died as close to penniless as most men can.

Then there is the story of Thomas F. Walsh, who, from an abandoned digging called the Gertrude, developed the Camp Bird gold mine in the San Juan country of southwestern Colorado. After proving the worth of this property by sending samples for assay and by taking out ore to the amount of $2,500,000, he sold the Camp Bird (which was by that time only one of 103 claims owned by him) for $6,500,000 and went on to a fortune beyond his belief. Included in it was the blue Hope diamond.

The story of gold rushes is pretty much the same the world over, with local variations dependent upon the region. In 1897, the rush was to the Klondike River basin in Alaska. There Robert Henderson, who had wandered north when the spell of gold in Colorado was fading, and George Carmack, a squaw man, panned gold in two different areas. Both eventually staked rich claims. The news leaked out as ships from Alaska docked at San Francisco and Seattle with treasure aboard. Within a matter of months, 33,000 would-be prospectors and miners were on their way to the Klondike on the edge of the Arctic Circle. They found mining conditions that none of them could have encountered anywhere before—earth that froze to impenetrable hardness and had to be thawed with fires, bit by bit, as the digging proceeded. The loosened alluvium had to be hoisted to the surface in buckets and left until the summer warmth thawed it again and the washing could begin.

Perhaps one of the reasons why there have been so few dramatic stories of uranium finds is that a fairly large proportion of the successful prospecting for these ores has been carried on by geologists in the employ of the U. S. Geological Survey, the Atomic Energy Commission, and private companies. The appealing element of a single man pitting his small resources and his energy in a gamble for wealth is generally lacking. Yet there is at least one such story that can be cited—the account of Vernon J. Pick, who left his home town in Minnesota because of financial difficulties. After salvaging what he could, he pulled out for the West, the

Colorado Plateau. There he invested some of his remaining money in a book and a Geiger counter, learned about uranium prospecting, and succeeded in establishing some claims which proved promising enough to bring him $9,000,000 in investment money.

Whether the ore the prospector is seeking is uranium or nickel, gold or lead, whether the gems being sought are sapphires or crystals of zircon, whether the prospector makes a business of his quest or plays at it pleasantly—if not profitably—on weekends, he will appreciate the salutation of uranium king Charles Steen, given on the occasion of his conferring the title Doctor of Uranium upon Jesse C. Johnson, Director of the Division of Raw Materials of the Atomic Energy Commission. "Greetings," said Steen. "Greetings to all men from the University of Hard Knocks and Raw Deals by its faculty of prospectors whose sun-blistered brows, bunioned feet, seatless pants, crock hair cuts, and insanely glittering eyes show that they have qualified as bone-fried desert country-type prospectors and uranium hounds. Prospectors who are thoroughly tested by blazing suns, freezing winds, reddish sandstorms, hungry scorpions, and the tall tales of crossroad and county-seat barroom liars and promoters. Those who have blistered their rumps riding burros and jeeps, have gone without baths and women, have trekked over deserts, climbed buttes, swum rivers, run rapids and jumped arroyos—not to mention a few claims; who have sat on cactus, killed buckskin out of season, rattled at rattlesnakes, eaten stewed rabbit and porcupine and in desperation tried a bobcat roasted in its own fur jacket; drunk skillet coffee, and smoked other men's cigarette snipes. Men who have located, mined, and milled uranium and who have drilled dry holes on their own without using widows' and orphans' money, and discovered that multimillion dollar lawsuits are actually filed."

And so we greet the readers of this book! Whether your goal is fun, a fund of new knowledge, a rock and mineral collection, or a platinum-plated and diamond-studded fortune—any or all of these—good prospecting!

Chapter 2

THE ART OF
MINERAL FINDING

Chapter 2

THE ART OF
MINERAL FINDING

The successful "rockhound" must have the best characteristics of the oldtime prospectors—who loved the outdoor life, were perpetually observant and curious about their surroundings, and who were, above all, persistent. The oldtimers always believed that, if they did not find what they were seeking this time, maybe next time they would. They possessed a boundless enthusiasm and an unshakable optimism that there was "gold in them thar hills." And they were frequently right.

They were right because they had learned what to look for—most of them were self-taught—and because they seldom thought of giving up. But they were limited in outlook, for most of them sought only gold, or perhaps silver—the chief sources of mineral wealth in those days.

Today's prospector should have more specific knowledge in order to succeed, for modern society needs and uses many kinds of mineral wealth other than the precious metals. Even these, moreover, can be more easily found with a better understanding of geologic structures, rock types, and mineral constituents. The modern prospector, too, can make use of suitable, and often inexpensive, equipment to make his search easier.

Whether you are a mineral collector, who enjoys nature and the fun of finding specimens for your collection, or a would-be prospector with a definite desire and purpose to look for wealth among the rocks and minerals of your area, you will find that the use of contour maps and handbooks (such as this one) and a continuing effort to enlarge your knowledge will be of the utmost value.

You may deliberately set out in search of mineral fortune, or you may keep a weather eye open for something promising while on a field trip for specimens. In either case, an acquaintance with the chief mining activities of your area—and of the country at large—is extremely helpful. In today's world, the economic, political, and military events of the nation swiftly affect mineral production. With changing needs, even a depressed mining industry may become prosperous, and minerals of little value at present may suddenly become valuable as the need for them arises or increases. The wary prospector will not neglect any earth material in his searches, whether it be metallic, nonmetallic, or mineral fuel.

It is important that you become familiar with rocks and minerals—especially those of your immediate vicinity. You will often find many excellent specimens on display in local museums, libraries, courthouses, and assay offices. Other places that sometimes display rocks and minerals of their region include banks, chambers of commerce, and stores. The shops that carry Geiger counters and other instruments for detecting radioactivity usually have good samples of uranium-bearing rocks with which to test the equipment. Other stores and offices of varying types, especially in mining regions, often have rocks and minerals on exhibit.

The serious mineral collector or prospector will become acquainted with these specimens, for they are a quick and readily accessible source of knowledge about the types of rocks and minerals common to his area. In the Pioneer's Museum at Colorado Springs, for instance, there is the personal collection of ore specimens belonging to

Shiny black obsidian is natural volcanic glass. This specimen shows a conchoidal fracture.

Granite is the most common of the coarse-grained group of rocks. It is an igneous rock. This specimen is called a porphyry, because one of the component minerals has "crystallized out."

Amygdaloidal basalt has a porous structure, and many minerals are found in its cavities. This specimen is from Mt. Somma, Italy.

Winfield Scott Stratton, famous for his Independence mine staked on the Fourth of July. Housed in a solid mahogany case, elaborately carved with figures of miners and burros, picks and shovels, the collection is said to represent every type of gold ore taken from the mines in the Cripple Creek district. In the Colorado State Museum in Denver, as another example, the State Bureau of Mines has separate cabinets to display the minerals found in each county in the state—certainly a great aid to the collector and prospector.

You will find that joining the mineral society or "rockhound club" in your area will help you to meet others who are interested in the art of mineral-finding—to make friends with whom you can compare specimens, see new ones, and discuss common problems. Many such societies take or-

ganized field trips, which prove especially helpful in learning more about rocks and minerals, collecting, and mining methods.

Rock vs. Mineral

Fundamentally considered, the earth's crust is built of *rocks. Minerals,* and often *natural glass,* are the individual substances that make up these rocks. A rock is usually an aggregate of two or more minerals, although a single mineral can occur on such a large scale that it may properly be termed a rock. Pure sandstone and quartzite, for example, have only one mineral—quartz. Other rocks made up of one mineral include dolomite, gypsum, and sulfur. Occasionally, rocks of this type have names that differ from that of the mineral of which they are composed; thus, limestone

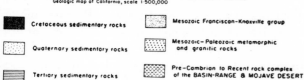

GEOLOGIC MAP OF CALIFORNIA
SHOWING LOCATIONS OF
TYPICAL COLUMNAR SECTIONS
IN RELATION TO
GEOMORPHIC PROVINCES
AND
GENERALIZED GEOLOGIC UNITS

Geomorphic provinces from Jenkins, Olaf P., 1938, Geomorphic map of California,
scale 1:2,000,000. Geologic units generalized from Jenkins, Olaf P., 1938,
Geologic map of California, scale 1:500,000.

▪ Cretaceous sedimentary rocks	▨ Mesozoic Franciscan-Knoxville group
▫ Quaternary sedimentary rocks	▨ Mesozoic–Paleozoic metamorphic and granitic rocks
▤ Tertiary sedimentary rocks	▨ Pre-Cambrian to Recent rock complex of the BASIN-RANGE & MOJAVE DESERT
	▨ Quaternary and Tertiary volcanic rocks of CASCADE RANGE and MODOC PLATEAU

········ Geomorphic province boundary
———— Geologic unit boundary
———— Fault

Geologic map of California
1. Northern Klamath Mountains
2. Redding Region
3. Warner Range
4. Northern Coast Ranges
5. West Side Sacramento Valley
6. Allegheny Area
7. Sierran Foothill Area
8. Mother Lode Area
9. Central Coast Ranges
10. West Side San Joaquin Valley
11. East Side Southern Sierra Nevada
12. Southern Inyo Range
13. Death Valley Area
14. Southern Sierra Nevada and San Joaquin Valley
15. Western Santa Ynez Mountains
16. Los Angeles Basin
17. Barstow Area
18. Julian District

consists of the mineral calcite, and rock salt contains only the mineral halite.

Minerals have a definite chemical composition and usually a regular internal structure, which may be expressed in outward form as *crystals.* Large bodies of volcanic glass may be quite devoid of mineral components. Obsidian is such a natural glass; it is seemingly uniform in appearance, yet so various are the proportions of its chemical constituents that no one formula can be written for it.

Some rocks are of organic origin, having been produced by plants or animals. Coal is this kind of rock, as is limestone when it is the result of deposits by algae and other forms of life.

Ore . . .

Ore is both a scientific and a commercial term. An ore is a rock or mineral body from which a metal may be profitably extracted. Without undergoing any actual change, a mineral deposit may cease to be classed as an ore, commercially, if the cost of mining it becomes unprofitable. If the price of a metal rises, however, or new mining methods make it again profitable, the deposit is regarded once more as an ore.

Stones . . .

Although used commonly, the term *stone* has no scientific standing—substances of the mineral kingdom are either rocks or minerals. It does have accepted usage, however, when applied to the commercial application of earth materials. Granite and marble are correctly referred to as building stones; diamond and opal can be called gem stones; and slate is a roofing stone.

And Gems

A *gem* may be either a rock or a mineral that is considered attractive enough by man to be used for personal adornment or other decoration. Most gems are true minerals, although some gems—such as lapis lazuli—are rocks. There are also a few gem materials, such as pearl and coral, that are of animal origin, and two—amber and jet—that have a vegetable ancestry.

The Heart of the Earth

Men once believed that beneath the earth's crust was a body of seething, hot liquid. Later, when this seemed unlikely, it was thought instead that a zone of liquid was the source of lava, or volcanic eruptions. But recent studies of earthquake (or seismic) waves show that the earth is essentially solid. The inner zones of our planet must be considerably heavier than the rocks visible at the surface. Research seems to suggest that the core may be composed of solid iron under terrific pressure, surrounded by molten iron, which is perhaps made turbulent by swirling currents and jet streams similar to those of the upper atmosphere.

In the outer part of the earth, there are occasional pockets of molten rock, even if no actual zone of such material exists. Possibly it is not truly molten, but semiplastic, kept thus by the pressure of overlying rock. When, perhaps as the result of overheating by radioactivity, this semiplastic rock melts, forcing its way toward the surface through fissures, it becomes *magma,* a mixture of melted rock and dissolved gases.

Igneous Rocks

As magma cools and solidifies (or crystallizes), it forms *igneous rocks.* Igneous means "fire-made" and refers to all the heat-formed rocks and minerals. Those rocks that have solidified beneath the surface, from magma, are termed *intrusive rocks;* rocks that have solidified upon the surface, from lava or volcanic fragments, are called *extrusive rocks.* Certain characteristics of each identify them as to type and origin.

Intrusive Rocks

Intrusive rocks cool slowly beneath the earth's surface and thus crystallize over a long interval of time. This process creates a coarse-textured rock of fairly large-sized crystals, often visible to the naked eye. Termed intrusive because they have "intruded" (or forced their way) into already existing rock, these bodies form the heart of the world's great mountain ranges and are visible only after millions of years of erosion. The most common example of an intrusive rock is granite. Other important intrusive rocks are gabbro, diorite, pegmatite, porphyry, syenite, and peridotite.

Extrusive Rocks

Lava rises rapidly to the surface and, exposed to the air, cools quickly. This rapid cooling prevents the growth of large crystals, and the resulting texture is always fine grained. Basalt, a dark, heavy, fine-grained rock, is a good example of an extrusive rock formed in this way. Pumice, made frothy by expanding gases, is another familiar example of an extrusive rock. It is found most frequently in the mouth of a volcano or in the top part of a lava flow, where the escaping steam rises most rapidly. The cooling process may occur so quickly that there is no evidence of crystallization at all, and a natural glass, such as obsidian, results. Extrusive rock is commonly thought of as originating in a volcano, but the typical cone or crater as seen in Vesuvius or Mauna Loa is not necessary in the formation of extrusive rock, for lava can issue quietly from open fissures without volcanic eruption. (The term *vulcanism* refers to the action of all molten rock, whether on the surface or beneath.)

Acidic Rocks

Igneous rocks range widely in chemical composition. Those rocks that are rich in silicon, such as granite, tend to be relatively light in weight and light colored as well. These are termed *acidic rocks* —also called *silicic rocks* because of their high content of silica.

Basic Rocks

As the amount of silicon is reduced and the con-

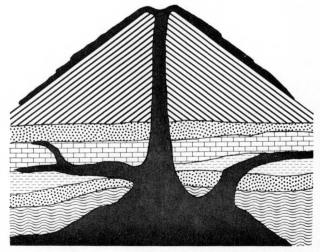

The cross section of an average volcano looks like this. Much of the lava breaks through the sides instead of coming over the top of the cone.

tent of iron and magnesium increases, the rocks become darker and heavier—they are then called *basic rocks*. Gabbro, with its extremely high iron content, is a typical basic rock.

Sedimentary Rocks

The forces of erosion eventually act upon even the most deeply buried igneous rocks. When this occurs, the rock will crumble and decompose under the influence of chemical and mechanical weathering, and particles will be dissolved in water or washed away by streams, blown by winds, or carried away by glaciers. Water is the most active factor in transporting *sediment,* as this weathered material is called, for rivers and streams continually shape the landscape and carry the sediment either as particles or in solution. Such material may settle out of the water because of its weight, or it may be precipitated chemically from a dissolved state. When this sediment becomes lithified into solid rock, it is termed *sedimentary rock*. When sand particles solidify, for instance, they become sandstone; gravel becomes conglomerate; clay or mud becomes shale. Rock salt and beds of borax are also sedimentary rocks.

Placers

Of particular interest to the prospector or mineral collector are the sedimentary deposits called *placers*. Placers contain heavy and often valuable minerals, such as gold and precious gems, which have been washed from higher elevations and carried downstream until a change in the current, an obstruction in the stream, or the sheer weight of the minerals themselves causes them to drop to the bottom. Gold, platinum, diamond, corundum (ruby and sapphire), spinel, zircon—all these and many other valuable metals and gems are familiar in placers. The oldtime prospector of the American West, with his gold pan, pick and shovel, and his burro, immediately comes to mind whenever placer mining is mentioned. *Sluicing, dredging,* and *hydraulicking* are variants of placer mining.

While placers laid down by streams are most common, there is another kind of placer to be found along beaches, where waves and currents separate the heavier minerals and lay them down along the coastline. The "black sands" of Califor-

nia, Oregon, and Japan consist of placers containing magnetite, chromite, and ilmenite.

How Sediment Becomes Rock

Eventually, loose sediment is transformed into firm rock. By *compaction,* the water is squeezed out and the particles are slowly solidified by the pressure of overlying sediments. If mineral matter is deposited between the grains, *cementation* takes place. *Recrystallization* refers either to the process of small particles growing into larger ones, or of new minerals forming in the spaces between other minerals.

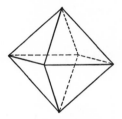

Spinel is commonly found in placer deposits in Ceylon. These crystals are red or blue and are cut into clear gems of considerable hardness.

Characteristics of Sedimentary Rocks

Because of the way in which they are formed, sedimentary rocks almost always have a distinctive parallel structure called *stratification* or *bedding*. The various layers or beds frequently differ from each other in mineral composition, color, and texture; a considerable difference in time may elapse between the deposition of successive beds.

Joints, which are groups of parallel cracks, are to be found in sedimentary rocks and in igneous rocks, but the shrinkage that causes them is the result of drying instead of cooling. If a layer of sedimentary rock is no longer horizontal, it has almost certainly been bent out of position since the time it was first deposited.

While stratification is the most notable property of the majority of sedimentary rocks, they are also characterized by the presence of concretions and fossils.

Concretions are nodules of mineral matter that differ from the layer of sediment in which they occur. They vary in size and shape from less than an inch in diameter up to many feet. If the nodules are hollow, they are called *geodes*. The interior of geodes may be lined with crystals—and thereby

Yuba Consolidated Industries

The gold dredge is a flat boat that recovers placer minerals by separating them from the sand and gravel in which they occur.

This dredge still stands near Fairplay, Colorado, where it was used to remove gold from deposits left by glaciers.

Standard Oil Company, New Jersey

Sedimentary strata in Oklahoma are being measured with a Brunton compass to determine their underground structure.

U. S. Geological Survey

The degree of "dip" of sedimentary rocks is readily measured with a Brunton compass, as here at Alcova, Wyoming.

Standard Oil Company, New Jersey

Hydraulicking is a method of placer mining that uses strong jets of water to loosen soft rock and free the valuable minerals. This scene is in Malaya.

British Information Services

become especially sought after by the mineral collector.

Fossils are to be found only in sedimentary rocks, because the extreme heat that forms the other types of rock usually destroys evidence of plant or animal life. Sedimentary rocks, on the other hand, are laid down in lakes or streams, swamps or oceans, and accumulate slowly over a long period of time. Remains or impressions of ancient animals or plants are thus preserved within the layers of rock, and can be studied to determine the relative age of the rocks and the kind of environment existing when the particular sediments were accumulating.

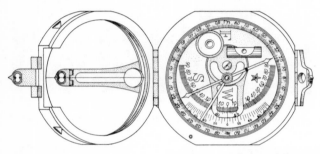

William Ainsworth & Sons

The Brunton compass, made in Denver, is world famous. It measures angles and directions from which maps can be drawn.

Some Sedimentary Rocks

Sandstone is made up of quartz fragments cemented together. When the fragments are larger —from the size of gravel up to that of boulders— the rock is called conglomerate. Spaces between the pebbles and boulders are filled with sand grains, for the most part, although clay, iron, or calcite may be present. Many conglomerates are the result of glacial action.

Shale is the world's most abundant sedimentary rock. The result of the compaction of mud, shale is made up of thin layers which split easily, showing a shell-like fracture.

Limestone is composed of calcite formed from either plants or animals, or by chemical means. It is familiar as a building stone; it is also seen as travertine deposited around mineral springs and as stalactites and stalagmites in caverns.

Because it is found in layers or beds, coal is considered a sedimentary rock. Originating in the decay and burial of dying plants, it first becomes peat, then lignite, then bituminous coal, and finally anthracite coal, as the pressure upon it is

increased and water and gases are forced out, leaving higher concentrations of carbon. The elimination of everything except carbon results in the formation of the mineral graphite.

Metamorphic Rocks

Metamorphic rocks, the third major type, have been formed by drastic changes in either an igneous or a sedimentary rock. *Metamorphism* is caused by heat, pressure, slow movement of the earth's crust, or the chemical action of gases and liquids. The resulting rock is so different in texture or mineral composition, or both, from the original that often it is impossible to tell whether the original rock was igneous or sedimentary. During metamorphism, the minerals of the original sedimentary or igneous rocks may grow into larger crystals, or they may form entirely new minerals.

Characteristics of Metamorphic Rocks

The most notable feature of metamorphic rocks is *foliation*—this is a distinctive layered, or banded, structure, which sometimes resembles the bedding of sedimentary rocks or even the flow structure of some igneous rocks, but which is due to the deforming or compression of existing rock. Foliation varies from thin sheets, characteristic of slate, to the coarse banding seen in gneiss. Joints are also a prominent feature of metamorphic rocks; they result from the gradual but intensive pressure exerted upon the rock.

Contact metamorphism occurs when intrusive igneous rock transforms the surrounding material. As the igneous rock cools and solidifies, it gives off its heat and expels its fluids. The adjoining rocks are

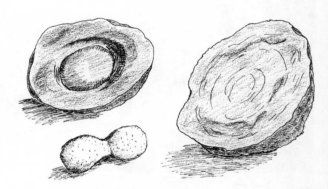

Lumps of mineral matter, known as concretions, are abundant in sedimentary rocks. These were found in Wyoming.

more or less drastically changed by this vigorous action. Carbonate rocks, such as limestone and dolomite, are affected in an especially profound way. Completely new minerals will be created, such as garnet, epidote, and idocrase. Ore deposits of certain metals, particularly wolfram (tungsten), also are a result of this process.

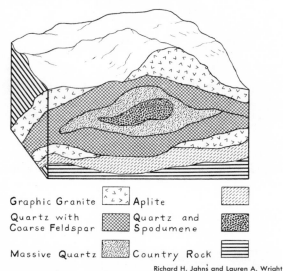

Graphic Granite   Aplite

Quartz with   Quartz and
Coarse Feldspar   Spodumene

Massive Quartz   Country Rock

Richard H. Jahns and Lauren A. Wright

The definite zoning of pegmatites is a recognized feature of many of them. The internal structure of this California pegmatite is typical.

Some Metamorphic Rocks

Shale is changed to slate by severe pressure. It is this pressure that creates the so-called slaty cleavage, which causes the rock to split into the thin, broad slabs that are its chief characteristic. Because of this property, slate is much used as a roofing stone.

The coarsest of all metamorphic rocks is gneiss, which may be derived from either an igneous or a sedimentary rock. Its mineral content is much the same as that of an average granite (quartz, feldspar, biotite, hornblende, and muscovite mica), but the grains are arranged in roughly parallel layers. These layers make up alternating dark and light bands, which are the most easily identifiable feature of gneiss. As the layers become closer together and more uniform in composition, gneiss grades into schist. Mica schist is a common and important rock.

Limestone turns to marble under metamorphism as the calcite is recrystallized. The soft, shimmering luster that appears has made marble prized through the centuries as a sculpturing and

building stone. The treasures of Greece show to what beautiful purpose marble can be put. The Lincoln Memorial in Washington, D. C., and the first Tomb of the Unknown Soldier in Arlington National Cemetery are both fashioned of Yule marble from the Rocky Mountains of Colorado.

A hard rock with a glistening appearance, quartzite is metamorphosed sandstone. As the name implies, it is made up almost entirely of quartz. While it sometimes resembles marble, it will not effervesce in acid, nor can it be scratched with a knife. Because a pure quartzite is the most durable of rocks, it can be found widely distributed throughout the mountain ranges of the earth. The Nelson Range in British Columbia, for example, is also known as the Quartzite Range.

The Company Each Mineral Keeps

Minerals are usually found in typical associations, a fact that makes them easier to recognize; for minerals, like people, can be known by the company they keep. These associations, which are the result of related origins, are of great importance to the collector or prospector. The task of recognizing rocks and minerals becomes far easier when you realize that certain minerals have a tendency to be found with certain other minerals,

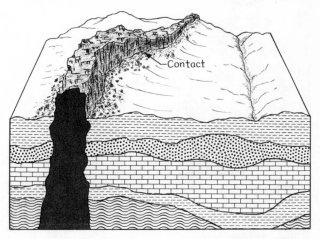

The contact between two different kinds of rock may contain minerals of interest. Such minerals have been brought up from beneath by rising solutions or produced by heat at the boundary itself.

having been formed under similar conditions. Tourmaline and beryl, for example, are often together in pegmatite, because they originate in the same way. Experience in the field will enable you to learn the various typical associations and characteristic rocks in which minerals are found.

Pegmatite

Pegmatite is an excellent example of how the prospector profits by coordinating this knowledge of association and occurrence. An extremely coarse igneous rock containing the same minerals as granite—mainly quartz, feldspar, and mica—pegmatite is the principal natural storehouse of exceptionally pure deposits of the more common minerals. It also contains valuable crystals and rare minerals to be found nowhere else. Readily observed aspects of pegmatite are a variable grain size and the distinctive intergrowths of microcline feldspar and quartz called graphic granite, or

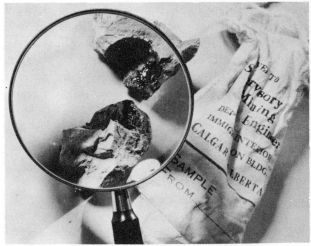

Standard Oil Company, New Jersey

Examining fossil shells in sedimentary rocks enables the geologist to date the age of the rocks. These in the Northwest Territories of Canada are hundreds of millions of years old.

Devil Postpile National Monument in California displays perfect examples of polygonal joints in basalt. They develop when the lava cools and shrinks.

Ewing Galloway

American Museum of Natural History

The rock called sandstone is made up of sand-size particles, which are usually grains of quartz. This particular sandstone occurs in California.

runite, referring to a resemblance to ancient cuneiform writing.

Irregularity of grain size is perhaps the most notable feature of pegmatite. Crystals range from less than an inch to colossal dimensions: one enormous crystal of spodumene (a lithium mineral) in the Black Hills of South Dakota weighed ninety tons and was forty-two feet long, while an entire quarry was operated in the Ural Mountains within a single crystal of feldspar. Such extreme variations in size, as well as in texture, mineral compo-

American Museum of Natural History

The thick wavy bands of light and dark minerals identify this rock as gneiss. Its origin is metamorphic—the change-over from an earlier igneous or sedimentary rock.

American Museum of Natural History

Larger particles than sand make conglomerate. This one is trassic conglomerate.

U. S. Geological Survey

Mica from Topsham, Maine, is characteristic of the pegmatite minerals in New England. White mica is referred to as muscovite.

sition, width, and position, occur even within the same pegmatite. Most pegmatite is acidic in composition and is often referred to as "giant granite." Basic pegmatite, in which quartz is minor or absent, does exist, but it is far less common.

Geologists believe that pegmatite is the last part of the magma (or molten rock) to solidify, retaining great amounts of steam and other vapors, which help to lower the temperature at which the magma becomes hard. It is this slowing of the process that makes it possible for minerals to grow to such gigantic sizes. During its solidification, the magma shrinks and cracks. The remaining liquid collects in these cracks or fissures, which are often shaped like caverns and then are called *miarolitic cavities*. "Pockets" of this sort—sometimes large enough for a man to stand up in—are a splendid source of outstanding crystals. (Rock cavities always provide an ideal growing place for crystals, for here they can grow without interference.) Other pegmatite solutions force their way into fractures in adjoining rock, perhaps to some distance from their origin. Such pegmatites are frequently found in metamorphic rocks adjacent to

Keokuk, Iowa, is a favored collecting locality for geodes such as this. The nature of the crystals inside remains a mystery until the boulder is cracked or sawed open.

Ward's Natural Science Establishment

huge bodies of granite. Most other pegmatites are enclosed in granite, however.

Rare minerals and fine gems not found elsewhere occur in pegmatite. Beryl, topaz, tourmaline, and zircon are among the gems found in this rock, often in substantial sizes. As many as fifty minerals have been identified in the deposits of each of several districts; besides those mentioned already, some of the best known are apatite, chrysoberyl, cassiterite, molybdenite, allanite and other rare-earth minerals, and various uranium and thorium minerals.

While the known masses of pegmatite may be almost any shape, a tabular form is most frequent, giving rise to the commonly used term *pegmatite dike.* Because the minerals—especially quartz—that make up pegmatite are harder and more resistant to erosion than other minerals, outcrops of pegmatite are abundant in the regions in which they occur and are usually quite easily spotted at or near the tops of knolls or ridges. In northern New England, for example, the exposed material is virtually unweathered and therefore quickly recognized. In the southern United States, however, weathering and the change of feldspar to clay may extend to a depth of a hundred feet. In spite of this, occasional "books" of mica and boulders of quartz, even if other signs are lacking, make it possible for the prospector and collector to find the deposit.

During World War II, the search for critical and strategic minerals was quickly expanded, leading to more detailed studies of pegmatite than had ever been carried on before. These studies emphasized the presence of zones, such as the *wall zone, border zone, intermediate zone,* and *core,* each having its own distinctive minerals. Such knowledge made possible the recovery of more minerals at a reduced operating cost. Because pegmatites are the source of rare-earth and radioactive minerals, as well as of cassiterite (ore of tin), beryl, and microcline feldspar (for the ceramic industry), this information has proved valuable. While field and laboratory studies on a massive scale have yielded much needed information, the methods of the old-time prospector are of proved effectiveness in the search for new deposits. Ordinary visual observation plus careful panning will enable the prospector to trace loose material upstream or uphill to its source. *Test pits, cross trenching,* and *core drilling* can

then determine the horizontal extent and zonal characteristics of the deposit.

Pegmatite is widely distributed throughout the world, but certain areas are famous for its occurrence. Outstanding deposits of pegmatite in the United States are found at Pala in California, in central Colorado, north-central New Mexico, Latah County in Idaho, the Black Hills in South Dakota, at Amelia in Virginia, in western North Carolina, and in Maine and Connecticut. Ontario and Quebec in Canada have numerous pegmatites; Brazil, Madagascar, South Africa, Sweden, and Norway also have a great many. Pegmatite is especially abundant in such high mountain ranges as the Alps, Pyrenees, Urals, and Andes.

Geodes

Geodes, the hollow concretions lined with crystals which we have mentioned as a feature of sedimentary rocks, are an exciting source of crystalline and gemmy growths. On the outside, they may appear simply as rough boulders, varying in size from an inch or so in diameter up to three or four feet or more, and weighing hundreds of pounds. Called "potato stones" in England, these ordinary-looking boulders reveal unexpected beauty when they are carefully broken open. The inner shell is often covered with successive layers of agate and other mineral deposits, and upon this base closely set, tiny crystals project into the hollow interior of the geode. Quartz crystals are most commonly found, and amethyst geodes are perhaps the most beautiful of all. Geodes also frequently contain calcite, millerite, and dolomite. In the United States, they are numerous in the Mississippi Valley, especially Illinois, Indiana, and Iowa. Brazil and Uruguay are noted for exquisitely colored amethyst geodes. Uruguay is also the source of excellent specimens of "water geodes," which contain large amounts of water; the liquid can be heard to splash when the geode is shaken. Like the more common "rattlebox geodes," which contain loose particles of sand or small pebbles, these curious rocks are spoiled if broken open.

Where You Can Find Minerals

Minerals are the stuff of which the earth is made and can be found everywhere. The mineral collector and prospector soon learn, however, that some

Brown Brothers

A mine dump is the heap of broken waste rock removed from a mine. Some are good places to collect specimens.

A quarry is an open mine. Enormous stone quarries can be visited in Vermont, where this one is located.

Brown Brothers

places are better than others. A few minerals—like happiness—can be found right in your own backyard. Sifting and examining garden soil will on occasion yield something of unexpected interest. Road cuts, building excavations, and tunnels often uncover creditable mineral specimens.

Sand and gravel banks contain much mineral material, especially quartz in all its diversity. Clay banks are good hunting grounds for concretions, geodes, and fossils, as well as specimens of pyrite, selenite (a clear variety of gypsum), and marcasite. Minerals in quantity may be found at the base of cliffs and in the beds of streams. Rock outcrops in any area should be examined carefully. Mineral specimens are sometimes found lying on top of the ground in fields or woods, but these are usually of inferior quality, being marred or stained by weathering.

Beaches and sand dunes, the desert floor, and dry or temporary lake beds are worthy places for mineral specimens. The sagebrush deserts of the western United States are exceptionally rich in minerals—quartz crystals, chalcedony geodes, pieces of obsidian, and pebbles of agate, opal, and petrified wood can simply be picked up off the ground. Flowerlike groups of crystals, and rosettes such as "barite rose" and "desert rose," are numerous. The temporary (*playa*) lakes of these arid regions contain borax, halite, and other saline minerals. Sulfur, quartz, and calcite are plentiful near the exits of hot springs. Certain heavy minerals are washed up by waves and currents along the beach.

Mines, quarries, placer operations, and smelters—and the heaps of waste rock surrounding them called *dumps*—are always productive. The dumps of mines and quarries are obviously a most promising source for the mineral hunter. Whereas the minerals to be secured depend chiefly upon the type of rock or mineral being produced—that is, a copper mine will furnish copper minerals, a feldspar quarry will supply pegmatite minerals—numerous other minerals are also found in and around most mines. Coal deposits are good sources of marcasite nodules and fossils.

Contacts

The prospector should learn early to recognize a *contact,* expecting to find in it something that may well prove to be worth his while. A contact is the surface of separation between two kinds of rock, each having been formed at a different time in geologic history. Contacts are natural places for minerals to be found, because the laying down of one sedimentary rock upon another, or the intrusion of an igneous rock into some other type, permits the development of a porous zone and the concentration there of mineral-bearing solutions. Furthermore, contacts are easy to locate, for the two formations at the contact are usually of unlike texture or color. There is often a conspicuous difference in the plant growth because of the variation in the soil.

Botanical Prospecting

Prospectors are even using differences in plant growth as a clue to the presence of metals beneath barren rock or a covering of sand and gravel. Known as *botanical prospecting,* this method should have a strong appeal to those who normally pay attention anyway to trees, shrubs, and flowers. Plants may be affected in a number of ways by an abundance of metal in the ground. Cobalt, for instance, produces white, dead patches on leaves. Molybdenum may result in a stunting of vegetation and a yellow-orange coloring. At Great Bear Lake in Canada, uranium causes wild blueberries to take on peculiar shapes. As early as 1818, Isaac Tyson, Jr., discovered chromium ores in Maryland and Pennsylvania by the comparative bareness of the mineralized area, made toxic by the excess of metal. It is only recently, however, that botanical prospecting has been taken seriously. Helen L. Cannon, stationed in Denver with the U. S. Geological Survey, is an outstanding American authority on this subject. Being able to recognize certain *indicator plants* can be profitable.

Wherever he lives, the mineral collector or prospector should seek out the mineral sources of his area, learn the appearance and characteristics of the rocks and minerals, and familiarize himself with the typical associations—the result of related origins—which make identification easier. He should learn something of geologic structure and seek constantly to improve his knowledge. Like the oldtime prospector, his success will depend on his knowledge and interest, plenty of perseverance—and a dash of luck.

Chapter 3

MINERALS OF
MOST VALUE

Chapter 3

MINERALS OF
MOST VALUE

The oldtime prospector thought chiefly in terms of gold or silver, but today's prospectors and mineral collectors are aware of the infinite future of a whole range of valuable minerals and rocks that have become essential to the modern economy. The so-called precious metals—gold, silver, and platinum—form only a fraction of this great group of economically valuable mineral resources. Furthermore, the number of useful earth materials is increasing steadily. Almost every mineral and rock has a potential commercial value as new applications are found, new ways to extract and process them are devised, and new needs are created for them by an expanding technology and an increasing population. The prospector today searches for uranium and thorium ores, for wonder metals such as beryllium, magnesium, titanium, and zirconium, for deposits of the rare-earth metals, and for the other minerals that promise so much for the future—among them lithium, boron, and selenium. Some of the minerals that he seeks are still little known, but as the information concerning them grows, so will their value and their multiplicity of uses. The 20th-Century prospector and collector, with his geologic maps and reports, his scientific equipment, and his greater knowledge, seeks and finds minerals of which the prospector in older days never dreamed.

Rare-Earth Metals

A closely related family of fifteen elements, the so-called *rare earths,* or *rare-earth metals,* are becoming increasingly important in industry. Although there has been a more widespread commercial use of them, only in recent years has it been possible to isolate some of the rare earths for proper research. Even now, large-scale operations are not always possible under current production methods.

Rare-earth metals and compounds have been used for carbon-arc electrode cores, in the glass industry, for photographic and projection equipment, and as an additive to alloys of steel and lighter metals. Research activities, the use for atomic energy of thorium (which occurs in some of the rare-earth minerals), and improved methods of production will almost certainly create a growing demand for the rare earths.

As far back as 1794, a Finnish chemist, Johann Gadolin, found a new metallic oxide in the earth near Ytterby, a village in Sweden. The mineral was first named yttria, and then later gadolinite. At that time, it was not realized that this oxide actually contained more than a dozen different elements. The fifteen metals which make up the rare-earth family are named lanthanum, cerium, praseodymium, neodymium, promethium, samarium, europium, gadolinium, terbium, dysprosium, holmium, erbium, thulium, ytterbium, and lutetium. Formerly termed "rare" because it was thought that they were, indeed, scarce, these strange-sounding metals are still not often found in concentrated deposits, even though they are more actually abundant in the earth's crust than some metals quite familiar to us.

Most of the rare-earth elements occur in the common rock-forming minerals, but only in very minor quantities. Feldspar and amphibole, for example, may contain a trace or even a small percentage of them, but such restricted occurrences are not readily available for research or commerce. Rare-earth elements are the chief constituents of monazite, allanite, and xenotime, but these minerals are only a minor part of the rock mass in which they themselves occur—as in granite pegmatite, for example. Primary concentrations are thus extremely rare, and many of these are not of sufficient size or quality to be mined. Beach and stream placer deposits have instead yielded the largest amount, except in California.

Monazite and bastnasite are the two main rare-earth minerals available in commercial quantities. Monazite is a phosphate of the cerium group of rare earths, and may contain lesser amounts of the yttrium group, with thorium making up 1 to 20 percent of the mineral. It is fairly hard and conspicuously heavy; it ranges in color from honey to reddish brown, and it has a resinous luster. Large reserves of monazite are available in India, Brazil, and the Union of South Africa, while known placer deposits of monazite are numerous in the United States—chiefly in Florida, Idaho, and South Carolina—but most of them are fairly limited in size.

Bastnasite is a fluocarbonate of the cerium group, with properties somewhat similar to those of monazite. It varies in color from pale tan to reddish brown, and has a resinous luster. In 1949, a large deposit of bastnasite was discovered in San Bernardino County, California, and this fluocarbonate of rare earths is the largest deposit of high-grade rare-earth metals known in the entire world. It contains very little thorium, however, and so is not in so much demand as monazite. Another deposit of bastnasite has been mined in New Mexico.

Prospecting for any of the rare-earth metals is greatly aided by the use of a Geiger counter or scintillation counter, because the thorium in monazite is radioactive; thorium in trace amounts led to the bastnasite discovery in California. Black sands are a good possible source of rare-earth minerals.

Whereas bastnasite is mined from open pits in California, monazite is mined by placer methods: dredges, gravity-concentration devices, and other processes similar to those used in gold mining. Because such concentrations usually contain numerous other minerals, including zircon, garnet, gold,

and platinum, intensive treatment is required to separate the marketable minerals from one another. As newer uses for the rare earths are developed, more satisfactory ways of recovering them will surely be devised.

The Wonder Metals

Several metals have been put into exceptionally expanded use since World War II. Research continues, and these *wonder metals*—including beryllium, magnesium, titanium, and zirconium—may well become major metals of the future.

Beryllium

Of the wonder metals mentioned, *beryllium* is the only one that is stable, light in weight, and with a high melting point. In spite of these virtues, beryllium had no useful application until American and German scientists began experimenting with its alloys after World War I. In late years, 80 to 90 percent of the beryllium used in the United States has gone into alloys, especially beryllium-copper alloys that are used in industrial tools, airplane parts, and radio and radar devices. Pure beryllium is used in X-ray-tube windows and as a source of neutrons. As a moderator and reflector of neutrons, it has increasing use in the field of atomic energy.

Crystals of beryl yield the metal beryllium, needed for space-age purposes. These came from South Dakota.

Until recently, the sole economic source of beryllium had been the mineral beryl, which also forms gems (emerald and aquamarine). It was recovered almost exclusively from pegmatites. New discoveries show that beryl can also occur in high-temperature ore veins. Furthermore, other beryllium ore minerals are coming to light, but they are nearly impossible to identify visually. For these reasons, the *Berylometer,* based on principles of radioactivity, was invented.

Beryl itself grows as a hexagonal crystal and in masses; its colors are pale or emerald green, light blue, yellow, and white. It has a glassy luster, a high degree of hardness, and a medium weight. Beryl-producing countries include Brazil, Argentina, South Africa, and the United States. In the United States, beryl is rather widespread, the main sources being the Black Hills of South Dakota. Colorado, North Carolina, and New Mexico also have appreciable deposits. Commercially, however, the United States relies upon imports from Brazil, Argentina, and Southern Rhodesia. New large-scale American discoveries, beginning in eastern Nevada, reveal the potential importance of beryllium-bearing minerals in addition to beryl; the silicates phenacite and bertrandite are especially significant.

Magnesium

The lightest structural metal known is *magnesium*. As early as 1808, Sir Humphry Davy obtained magnesium metal in an impure state, and by 1833, Michael Faraday had prepared magnesium by electrolysis of fused anhydrous magnesium chloride. Robert Bunsen developed an electrolytic cell in 1852, and it was with a modification of this cell that the first manufacture of magnesium on a commercial scale began in Germany in 1908. By the following year, magnesium was in limited industrial production and use. Until World War I, Germany was the world's only source of magnesium.

When imports from Germany were halted, the United States began active production of magnesium. During the years that followed, the supply of magnesium increased slowly, and with the advent of World War II, its production in the United States expanded on a scale unequaled by any other basic metal industry. Magnesium became a substitute for aluminum, copper, lead, and zinc. It was used extensively in airplanes and in precision instruments, in photography, signal flares, and in incendiary bombs. In the years since the war, magnesium has become a widespread structural metal for civilian needs, much used in airplane and automobile manufacture, for structural shapes and sheets, and in a great variety of items ranging from artificial limbs to cameras, field glasses, and surveying instruments. Extensive use of magnesium is made in the manufacture of portable tools and other items where lightness of weight is essential. It is also much used in the preparation of other metals. Magnesium oxide is a principal refractory used to line high-temperature furnaces and kilns.

Magnesium is abundant throughout the world; the United States is completely self-sufficient in its supply of magnesium minerals, and enough of the metal could be taken from the ocean to last a million years or more. There are about sixty magnesium-bearing minerals, the most widespread being magnesite, dolomite, brucite, olivine, and serpentine. The first four mentioned, plus sea water, sea-water bitterns, and well brines, account for nearly all the production of magnesium compounds.

Magnesite occurs in coarse and finely crystalline forms. Coarsely crystalline varieties come from Washington and Nevada; the denser magnesite is mined almost entirely in California. Foreign reserves in Austria and elsewhere are large.

Dolomite, a double carbonate of calcium and magnesium, includes the high-magnesian limestones. In fact, most dolomites are really dolomitic limestones, and these deposits are widespread in the United States and abroad.

The only known American deposit of brucite—a whitish mineral that looks like talc or mica—is at Gabbs, Nevada.

Titanium

Titanium is another of the wonder metals of the present century. Gems, metals, and pigments contain this element, which has been called the outstanding new metal of our era. Although titanium is perhaps the ninth most abundant element in the crust of the earth, only two minerals—ilmenite and rutile—yield it commercially. Furthermore, it is difficult to separate from them.

Nearly 99 percent of the ilmenite used industrially in the United States goes into the manufacture of titanium dioxide for high-opacity pigments. The whitest of all paints, titanium white, has an opacity twice that of zinc oxide and three times that of lead oxide. It can be mixed with other pigments without any decrease in this property. Titanium paints are used for enamels and lacquers, for outside white paints, and in the manufacture of paper, rubber, floor coverings, textiles, and artificial teeth.

Rutile is used primarily for welding-rod coatings. Other uses include chemicals, ceramics, and fiber glass.

There is a growing utilization of titanium metal and titanium alloys, which will steadily increase as extractive and metal-working processes are developed and improved. Low in density, and halfway between silver and stainless steel in color, titanium metal combines lightness, strength, and resistance to corrosion. Titanium alloys approach alloy steels in tensile strength and hardness, and they are far stronger than aluminum alloys. Pure titanium metal is being used more and more, especially in the aircraft industry for airframes and power plants. The Navy makes good use of titanium's strong resistance to the corrosiveness of sea water. Color-removing chloride is made from titanium; smoke screens and skywriting make use of titanium tetrachloride. Various other titanium compounds have a multiplicity of uses.

Because the ore minerals of titanium are heavy and resistant to weathering, they accumulate as placers. The titanium minerals originate as accessory minerals in igneous rocks, from which they are released by weathering. They are then found in beach and stream placers in association with monazite, zircon, cassiterite, and other valuable minerals. Ilmenite also occurs in massive igneous deposits of magnetite.

The United States, India, Norway, Canada, and Finland are the leading producers of ilmenite. Allard Lake, Quebec, has the largest known deposit. Australia has nearly a monopoly on the output of rutile.

Titanium, a "wonder metal" of growing importance, is extracted from rutile. This crystal of rutile was found in Georgia.

Zirconium

The *Nautilus,* America's first atomic-powered submarine, was made possible by another wonder metal—*zirconium.* Zirconium oxide was discovered in 1789, and in 1824, the metal itself was isolated. Before World War I, the use of zirconium was largely experimental and confined primarily to Germany and Austria. Further use, both military and industrial, has been made of zirconium through the years, but it was not until the atomic-energy program was accelerated that real interest was aroused in this metal. Zirconium has been found to be the most satisfactory structural material in nuclear reactors. It is used for electronic tubes, flashlight bulbs, electrical condensers, X-ray filters, and lamp filaments. The latest use of zirconium-steel alloys has resulted in quality armorplate and high-speed projectiles; zirconium-nickel alloys make sharp cutting tools.

The oxide of zirconium is one of the most refractory substances known. Consequently, it is used for chemical-resisting furnace bricks, high-temperature cements, crucibles, and laboratory equipment. It is also used increasingly to give opacity to enamels and lacquers, as an abrasive, as an insulator for heat and electricity, and in numerous other applications.

Zircon is virtually the sole commercial source mineral for zirconium. It is found in stream, beach, and dune sands in the United States, Australia, Brazil, and scattered countries in Asia and Africa. It comes entirely from placer deposits worked primarily for ilmenite and rutile. Other heavy minerals are by-products. Mining costs are relatively low, in comparison with the costs of transportation and marketing, due to the remoteness of many of the richer deposits.

Zircon is found in hues ranging from colorless through varying shades of yellow to grayish green and reddish brown. The transparent varieties are valued as a gem. A silicate mineral, zircon is hard as well as heavy, and has a bright luster.

Uranium and Thorium Ores

Virtually unknown except to specialists before World War II, *uranium* is perhaps the most discussed mineral substance in the world today. We think of it first in connection with atomic weapons, of course, but the peace-time uses of the future seem unlimited. These uses in industry, agronomy, and medicine are being investigated intensively, and commercial nuclear power in the coming decade seems certain.

While more than 150 uranium-bearing minerals are known to exist, only a few are common. The five primary uranium-ore minerals are pitchblende, uraninite, davidite, coffinite, and brannerite. These were formed by deep-seated hot solutions and are most commonly found in veins or pegmatites. The secondary uranium-ore minerals—altered from the primary minerals by weathering or other natural processes—are carnotite, tyuyamunite and metatyuyamunite (both very similar to carnotite), torbernite and metatorbernite, autunite and meta-autunite, and uranophane.

Primary Uranium Minerals

The most important uranium mineral is pitchblende, so called because it has a luster like that of pitch. Nearly pure pitchblende is called uraninite; it comes in small crystals, one to three inches in length, and its chemical composition is uranium oxide. Pitchblende contains from 50 to 85 percent uranium oxide and may also contain lead, helium, rare earths, zirconium, and other impurities. Although sometimes grayish or greenish, pitchblende is more often black. It may be coated with an iron crust or various colorful secondary uranium minerals. A powdery, green coating is due to the presence of nickel; a powdery, pink coating, to cobalt. Even though most often pitchy in appearance, pitchblende is sometimes dull, sometimes glossy, and even occasionally banded or fibrous. It is moderately hard and decidedly heavy. Pitchblende occurs in irregular lumps, and it is often found with iron, copper, lead, cobalt, nickel, silver, and bismuth minerals.

The experiments of the Curies with radium were conducted on pitchblende from Joachimsthal in Bohemia, which is now a part of Russian-controlled Czechoslovakia and contains one of the three largest bodies of pitchblende in the world. Another major deposit is situated at Great Bear Lake, Northwest Territories, Canada. The greatest mines of pitchblende have been in the Congo, where weathering has produced many of the secondary minerals; the incomparable Shinkolobwe mine is now reported as exhausted.

First discovered in 1955, the uranium mineralization at Ambrosia Lake, New Mexico, ranks first in the United States in total reserves. Here, coffinite is mixed with an asphaltic substance.

Secondary Uranium Minerals

Most secondary uranium minerals are bright orange, yellow, or green, and they occur in earthy or powdery masses, as groups of tiny crystals, or as flat plates. All have a lower uranium content than pitchblende. Of these secondary minerals, carnotite is the most familiar. A hydrous vanadate of potassium and uranium, carnotite is an important source of both uranium and vanadium, containing 50 to 55 percent uranium oxide. Copper is also found in association with carnotite, making it a profitable mineral to mine, indeed; it was formerly also a source of radium. Pure carnotite is bright yellow, resembling sulfur, but impure carnotite is greenish or brownish. Carnotite is chiefly found in the Colorado Plateau area of western Colorado, eastern Utah, and northern Arizona and New Mexico, where it is scattered in sandstone or found in rich masses around petrified wood, carbonized wood, and fossil bones—including those of dinosaurs.

Most of the numerous secondary uranium minerals, except those in the Congo, have little commercial value. Two of American occurrence, however, are torbernite (and metatorbernite) and autunite (and meta-autunite). The autunites are light yellow or greenish yellow in color, and they fluoresce bright, yellowish green under ultraviolet light. The torbernites are bright green and resemble autunite, but do not fluoresce. These minerals contain about 60 percent uranium oxide. They are often found with decaying vegetation, peat, lignite, coal, fossil plants, and oil.

Thorium—And Its Uses

Thorium may have an important future in nuclear power, as experiments seem to indicate that it can become an economical source of fissionable uranium-233 in the *breeder reactor,* producing more material than is burned in the fuel system of the reactor. As this becomes so, thorium represents newer and broader mineral reserves of nuclear energy. Over the long term, thorium seems likely to contribute more energy than coal, oil, and natural gas combined.

Monazite, a phosphate of rare earths, is by far the chief source of thorium. A pure commercial thorium nitrate is made from monazite concentrates. By igniting the thorium nitrate, thorium oxide is obtained. This chemical has long been used in the production of gas mantles for street lighting, kerosene lamps, and gasoline lanterns. It is utilized as a refractory and in the petroleum industry as a catalyst. It is employed in the production of tungsten filaments for vacuum tubes. Thorium salts are added to medicinal creams and lotions. As a constituent of magnesium alloys that possess remarkable strength for missiles and supersonic aircraft, thorium metal has its largest nonenergy use.

The Precious Metals

Since recorded history, gold and silver have been valued by man above all other metals. Great events have been fashioned by them; civilizations have risen or declined because of them. Even now, with our multiplicity of extraordinary metals, gold and silver, and the more modern platinum, are referred to as the precious metals.

Gold

Gold is prized for its intrinsic worth and for its use as ornament and decoration. For 2,000 years, its value has remained relatively stable. Today, because its price is fixed while the costs of mining and labor increase, gold (together with silver) seems not so attractive as a mining venture.

Native gold in California occurs both as crystals and in nuggets. The proportion of pure gold in the mineral varies, the rest being silver.

Because of this fixed price, however, there is the advantage of a sure market for any gold that the prospector might discover. And, of course, gold mining can return to favor at any time in case of

deflation or a return to the gold standard. There was, for example, a greatly increased interest in gold prospecting after the price was raised in 1934 from $20.67 an ounce to $35.00, in order to stimulate the economy. Prospectors swarmed everywhere, dumps were reworked, and a modern version of the oldtime gold fever was revived. Always, the lore and fascination of gold remains.

Gold is found in varying quantities in nearly every country in the world. Gold-bearing rocks

Gold tellurides are compounds of gold and tellurium. When roasted, the tellurium is driven off and gold remains on the surface.

are of many kinds and geologic ages, although most of the known deposits are associated with certain typical rocks and are of either very early or comparatively recent age. Gold deposits are found chiefly in the vicinity of acidic igneous intrusions, and they represent magmatic, contact-metamorphic, replacement, and cavity-filling types.

Three general sources of gold are recognized: (1) placers of native gold, always associated with some silver; (2) veins containing gold and little else, except quartz and other nonmetallic (*gangue*) minerals; and (3) base-metal ores—such as pyrite and chalcopyrite—which yield gold as a by-product. Besides its native form, gold occurs in compounds as tellurides; alloyed with much silver as electrum; and with mercury as amalgam.

California leads all the other states in total gold production, but the Homestake mine in South Dakota is the largest in the country. Colorado is the second-ranking gold state, and Cripple Creek holds second place among individual districts.

Silver

Silver has long been a medium of exchange; some sources estimate that one-third of the world's output of silver is still in circulation as coinage. Its use in jewelry and other items of personal adornment is no longer so strongly in fashion as formerly, but there is emphasis today on its use in the arts and industries. Alloyed with 7½ percent copper, it becomes standard-grade "sterling silver" for tableware. The photographic and electroplating industries make vast uses of silver; without this white metal, the motion picture industry (with its "silver screen") would have been impossible. Silver is being used more and more frequently in the chemical, electrical, and bearing industries. Silver solders and brazing alloys are widely used in joining pipes, forming mechanical assemblies, and making electrical connections. During World War II, the bearings of aircraft engines and mechanized equipment were plated with silver to insure longer life and heavier duty.

Silver, like gold, occurs in three ways. As native silver, it is a splendid mineral found in thickly tangled wires or in solid masses, sometimes of huge size. Natural silver compounds include argentite, cerargyrite, and pyrargyrite; some such minerals are exceedingly rich and almost as valuable as native silver itself. Finally, silver exists as a chemical impurity in certain base-metal minerals—galena, for example—from which it is obtained as a by-product.

Virtually all the world's supply of silver comes from North and South America, the Soviet Union, and Australia. Mexico is now the principal source. A single volcanic mountain in Bolivia (Potosí) is believed to have yielded over one billion ounces of silver since 1544. Cobalt, Ontario, is famous for its "silver sidewalk," a great solid block of nearly pure silver. The Rocky Mountain states are the chief producers of silver in the United States.

Platinum

The increasing value of *platinum* as an industrial metal, its scarcity, and the wide-open world market today make it highly sought after by the shrewd prospector. Platinum is the most important and most abundant of the six white "platinum metals" —namely, platinum, palladium, iridium, osmium, rhodium, and ruthenium. These metals are not only associated with one another, but they are naturally alloyed so that no one of them is ever found alone.

All the platinum metals are extremely heavy and have high melting points. Owing to an iron content that ranges from 5 to 15 percent, they are slightly magnetic. They occur in flakes, small grains, and sometimes substantial nuggets.

In addition to the native metals, only one other platinum mineral, known as sperrylite, is of economic importance. Most present-day platinum is actually a by-product of the refining of ores mined principally for nickel or chromium, with which platinum is geologically affiliated—always in basic igneous rocks or in placers derived from them.

Platinum is a fairly modern metal, until recently used primarily for jewelry and decorative work; all six metals of the platinum group, however, are now being used more and more in industry. They are particularly essential to the chemical and electrical industries, in which they are used for resistance and contacts in delicate instruments; for containers, wire, coils, and electrodes in X-ray equipment; and for large acid stills. As a catalyst for producing high-octane gasoline, platinum puts pep in the nation's automobiles. Because of its sleek beauty, platinum has been much desired as a setting for diamonds.

Colombian aborigines were apparently the first people to find platinum, which they made into ornaments. When introduced into Europe in the 18th Century, platinum was not regarded seriously. In fact, counterfeit coins were made of crude platinum and then coated with gold. Platinum was discovered in Russia in 1819, and that country was the world's main producer of the metal for almost a century. At one time, the Russian government authorized genuine platinum coinage.

The world's supply of the platinum metals today comes from the Union of South Africa, Canada, and the Soviet Union. The United States relies for its domestic production almost entirely upon a small yield in the Goodnews Bay district of Alaska.

Quartz and Other Gem Minerals

There are more than 200 varieties and subvarieties of quartz, the most abundant of all the useful minerals. Quartz is familiar to everyone because it is widespread throughout the world; yet, just because of this availability, as well as because of its beauty in most of its many varied forms and colors, quartz remains the favorite mineral of the specimen collector. Marvelous collections of quartz specimens attest to the never-ending satisfaction of the study and acquisition of this diversified mineral. Its hardness and fine texture, furthermore, make it the favorite gem stone of the amateur lapidary. Any lapidary will declare that, from rock crystal to amethyst, from agate to onyx, there is no mineral easier or more satisfying to work with than quartz, or one that rewards his efforts with a more attractive jewel.

U. S. Geological Survey

Veins of pyrargyrite, an ore of silver, penetrate this specimen of quartz from Tonopah, Nevada.

You will read in detail in Chapter 10 about the quartz minerals and their uses. Chapter 9 deals with other gems of interest and value to the prospector and collector.

Up-and-Coming Minerals

So quickly are new discoveries made and new processes devised in this rapidly changing century, so swiftly are new uses found for long-existing natural resources, that it is amazing and exciting to contemplate the developments that lie ahead in the field of minerals and metals. Three familiar substances, for example—boron, lithium, and selenium—have acquired new and different uses in their applications to nuclear energy.

Boron

Boron is commonplace in the forms of borax and boric acid; few other chemicals, indeed, have as many and varied uses. As an antiseptic and a flux,

in medicine and cleansing, boron compounds are well known. But with the advent of atomic energy, with further experimentation, with alloys, and in the growing petroleum industry, boron has taken on a whole new aspect.

The newest and perhaps the most important development concerns nuclear energy. Boron absorbs neutrons. Atomic reactors are shielded with a material named Boral, which consists of boron carbide and aluminum. Potential uses appear to be increasingly significant. In the oil industry, boron compounds have been used for their antiknock properties in gasoline for high-compression engines, and as dehydrating agents, catalysts, and fire retardants. They have also been tested for possible value as jet and rocket fuels. During World War II, it was discovered that adding boron to low-alloy steel makes it possible to reduce substantially the proportions of other alloying agents.

Boron is an obvious constituent of magmas, inasmuch as igneous rocks contain borosilicates—tourmaline is one of them—and boric acid is present in hot springs. Commercial sources of boron include bedded deposits beneath old dried lakes (called playas), the brines of saline lakes and marshes, encrustations around lakes and playas, and hot springs and fumaroles (gas vents).

Known and used for centuries, the mineral called borax first came from Tibet. Later, Italy and then South America were the world's source of supply. In the 1880's, there began the colorful history of borax mining in Death Valley, California, made famous by the "twenty-mule teams" used to haul the borax to Mojave. Other borate minerals—colemanite, ulexite, and kernite, all lightweight white minerals—have in turn succeeded borax as the principal sources of boron, but California still retains the leading position in this industry.

Lithium

Lithium, the lightest metal known to man, was

Borax, shown in this California crystal, is a useful mineral in the manufacture of many modern products.

discovered 150 years ago, but little attention was paid to it until quite recently. It has risen from obscurity to a period of spectacular growth in little more than a decade. Lithium weighs only about half as much as water. Silvery-white, softer than lead, it imparts a crimson color to a flame. It is very active chemically and combines readily with other elements. When heated, it combines with most gases and will even absorb traces of them.

Lithium metal is alloyed with aluminum, magnesium, and zinc for airplane parts, although this is still in the experimental stage as far as extended commercial use is concerned. Perhaps the most significant and large-scale application of lithium is in the making of the hydrogen bomb; however, public information as to its exact function has not yet been released.

It is the lithium compounds rather than the metal itself that have the most numerous and varied applications. These range all the way from mineral waters and lithium tablets to dry-cell and storage batteries, from the red coloring of fireworks and signal rockets to the curing of meat and the manufacture of dental cement. A goodly proportion of the lithium compounds are used in lubricants as "all-purpose greases." Other major uses are in ceramics and in special glasses such as sealed-beam headlights, radio, television, and radar tubes, and neon tubing.

Lithium is recovered commercially from pegmatite dikes and related veins as the minerals spodumene, lepidolite, petalite, and amblygonite, and from brines in the compound dilithium sodium phosphate. This widespread element is also present in sea water and in many mineral springs and clay beds. Lithium in large quantities occurs mainly in the United States, Canada, and central and southern Africa.

The most important lithium-ore mineral in the United States is spodumene, mined in the Black Hills of South Dakota, in the Kings Mountain district of North Carolina, and in New Mexico and California. Spodumene occurs as whitish, lath-shaped crystals, often growing to unbelievable size. The largest recorded crystal was extracted at the Etta mine in South Dakota; it measured six feet in diameter and forty-two feet in length.

Lepidolite and amblygonite are two other important lithium minerals. Lepidolite occurs as a granular aggregate of pale-violet flakes, usually fine-grained, and is a complex silicate of aluminum, potassium, and lithium. Amblygonite, which somewhat resembles feldspar, is the richest lithium mineral, but no large deposits are known.

Selenium

Selenium—"a chameleon among metals"—is a by-product obtained from the refining of copper ores, mostly in the United States and Canada. Prior to World War I, it was considered troublesome by smeltermen, and most of it was discarded. It was first used as a substitute for manganese in decolorizing glass when manganese was in short supply during the war. Because selenium did this job better, its use was continued, and the glass in-

Foote Mineral Company

A lithium-bearing mineral, spodumene may grow into crystals of enormous size. Its occurrence is in pegmatites.

dustry took most of the selenium produced. Then, with the advent of World War II, selenium was taken over by the rectifier industry. Selenium rectifiers had been known since 1884, but the military situation brought them into extensive use. Selenium dry-plate rectifiers are employed to change alternating current to direct current. In recent years, miniature rectifiers for radio and television sets have eliminated bulky transformer and rectifier tubes, saving over half a pound of copper and seven and one-half pounds of steel in each television set. One of the most interesting uses of rectifiers is in guided missiles.

Currently regarded as a strategic material, therefore, selenium is also employed extensively in the making of glass and ceramics and in the chemical, rubber, drug, and pigment industries. Because it conducts electricity only when exposed to light, it is used for automatic devices in "electric eyes," burglar alarms, streetlights, and other electronic devices. It has been called the universal solvent for plastics. A seemingly endless number of uses for selenium have appeared over the years. Since selenium is a by-product, its output depends on the demand for copper. As more uses are discovered and developed, there will be an increasing demand for larger quantities of selenium, and new sources must be found by the prospector.

Other Up-and-Coming Minerals

To suggest the opportunities awaiting the prospector in other up-and-coming minerals, let us refer briefly to some of the metals just now appearing on the scientific and industrial horizon. *Cesium,* the first element discovered with the spectroscope (1860), had little value for nearly a century, but as an ion rocket-engine fuel, it may well hasten the development of space travel. A laboratory curiosity until after 1950, *niobium* (better known in the United States as *columbium*) is being increasingly recommended for use in high-temperature environments. *Gallium* melts in the palm of your hand and remains liquid for 1,950 degrees C. This remarkable metal offers a challenge to the electronics engineer. *Germanium,* not long ago regarded by metallurgists as a downright nuisance, now serves as a semiconductor in transistors and diodes. The age of the transistor has also brought into prominence such an otherwise rare metal as *indium;* in 1924, the world's entire supply could have been held in a teaspoon. The ability of the metallurgist to refine *thallium* (which has infrared applications) and other metals to a purity exceeding 99.999 percent—a perfection existing only in theory a short while ago—has opened fantastic new vistas to the searcher for, and user of, metals.

Chapter 4

THE PROSPECTOR
IN THE FIELD

Chapter 4

THE PROSPECTOR
IN THE FIELD

In an earlier era, when outdoor life was more of an everyday affair than it is now, we used to say that the difference between a tenderfoot and an oldtimer was that the oldtimer always tried to make himself as comfortable as possible in a given situation, while the tenderfoot apparently tried to find out how much misery he could endure and still keep going.

Although times have changed, and the present-day outdoorsman, whether tourist, sportsman, or prospector, has comforts available beyond the wildest dreams of the pioneer, the point is still well made. A good night's sleep and adequate food remain indispensable, and with them, your outdoor life can be all you hope for when you start out on a trip. When properly done, prospecting is hard, exhausting physical work, but with comfortable sleeping equipment and suitable food, no experience is more rewarding to those who are physically and mentally fitted for it.

There can be as many variations in a suggested checklist of equipment as there are individual prospectors and places where they might wish to go. Nevertheless, certain basic needs must be met by anyone in any place. Some of these needs are discussed here under various headings—not in order of importance, nor to meet all possible conditions, but to give a general idea of the problem of being properly equipped, yet without having too much burden to lug around. This, again, depends upon the locale of your trips and your mode of transport, as well as upon your individual preferences. One seasoned outdoorsman insists upon carrying a down pillow in his bed roll, though most of us would think it superfluous. Your per-

sonal and car needs should be considered carefully.

Clothing

The right clothing, including footgear, is essential. Most people find that a medium-height laced boot is the most satisfactory footwear, worn with one pair of heavy wool socks over a lighter pair, either wool or cotton as you wish. Wool in direct contact absorbs perspiration, and is more comfortable in summer and much warmer in winter; the heavy outer socks provide additional cushion. You should provide two pairs of boots, as well as a lighter pair of shoes to wear around camp. Take plenty of socks so that you can wear a clean pair every day, especially in hot weather. Hob nails, while they lengthen the life of the soles in rocky country, are heavy, hard on the feet, and conduct both heat and cold right through a leather sole which, without them, is excellent insulation. If the going is rough, your boot heels will wear out as fast as your soles anyway—perhaps faster.

Your outer clothing will vary according to locality, but here again, wool is the most satisfactory, even on the desert. A wool shirt will afford more protection from the sun than any other fabric, and in desert country, the air cools off so much and so fast after sundown that wool feels very good.

In extremely cold weather, several layers of light, loose, wool garments are much more effective in retaining warmth than fewer, heavier ones. If woolen trousers or shirts get soaked in fording a stream or in a heavy downpour, they soon dry comfortably, while cotton and other fabrics remain clammy and chilly. In most temperate climates, an outfit should include a good wind- and water-resistant jacket with a wool lining, for use on days when it is called for, and especially around camp after nightfall.

Leather gloves, not necessarily heavy but of work weight, will save your hands in working with rocks and gathering firewood, besides being desirable in cold weather. In the bright western United States sunlight, a pair of good-quality sun glasses are required, whether you are working on bare ground or traveling over snow or water. Snow blindness is serious, and much the same bad effect can be "caused by" the hot desert sun. No longer are dark glasses considered the mark of the "movie-star type." Many an oldtimer will admit, in a moment of candor, that his eyesight would now be better if he had not scorned them during his active years.

Camp Equipment

The necessary camp equipment is shelter and a good bed. Beyond that, what one takes is pretty well dictated by his transportation and what he wants in the line of labor-saving things. It is perfectly possible to be out for weeks with no cooking articles except a frying pan, coffeepot, and kettle, but it is much easier if you have such things as a Dutch oven, more kettles and pans, a can opener, plates, cups, and so forth.

It is probably safe to assume that almost all prospectors and collectors will have a motor vehicle, so that neither weight nor moderate bulk are factors of great moment.

In that case, you will want a tent. Probably the most satisfactory is the wall tent; an eight-by-ten-foot wall tent with a four-foot wall—the common two-foot wall takes away the usability of about half the floor area—is large enough for two people and can accommodate four if it must, although in wet weather four men and their gear will crowd its space.

Select as level a place as possible in which to pitch the tent, and in rainy weather, a trench around it will take off the drainage, both from the surrounding ground and the tent itself. Locate your trench so that it will catch the water running from the roof of the tent and carry it away. A tent shrinks temporarily when it gets wet, so that it is necessary to keep loosening the guy ropes to prevent the tent pegs from being pulled out. And be forewarned that if you touch the inside of a wet tent, the water will keep on leaking through as long as the rain falls.

Other types of tent are also satisfactory, such as the "umbrella" with a single pole in the center, but avoid the straight "A" or "pup" tent unless you are reasonably certain of good weather. Your comfort will be increased if the tent has a canvas floor sewed to the side walls, with a threshold at the door several inches high, but it also adds considerably to bulk and weight. It does have decided advantages in a desert country or wherever else there are crawling pests, and in cold weather it avoids drafts at floor level.

Any number of good sleeping bags are on the market. An air mattress—not too highly inflated— is not only an aid to comfort but a time-saver in making camp, since it avoids the chore of getting every little clod, stone, or stick out of your bed place. It is also much less bulky than the comfort equivalent in quilts or blankets. An air mattress is, however, a cold thing to sleep on in cold weather, and extra insulation should be provided beneath you.

Cooking Equipment

The locality you are working in, as well as your type of transportation, will usually determine whether you will take a gasoline stove or depend upon a wood fire. A two-burner gasoline camp stove is quick and easy to set up, eliminates the problem of firewood, and may be moved inside a tent in wet or stormy weather. On the other hand, its capacity is limited to two cooking jobs, while other food gets cold or awaits its turn; it involves a certain amount of weight and bulk; and it requires special nonleaded gasoline.

If wood is available, a campfire provides warmth and unlimited cooking capacity, including the chance to cook a pot of beans or a stew in a Dutch oven in the ashes. For chopping purposes, take along a good single-bitted ax about three pounds in weight, which will be handy around camp. Besides your normal supply of

Socony Mobil Oil Company

Pack trains are still indispensable for penetrating remote country in the hunt for mineral wealth. This exploration party is heading for the back country of British Columbia.

wooden kitchen matches, it is worthwhile to have several small boxes of waterproof matches stuck away in your gear, for they will burn under any conditions.

The following list of cooking equipment is only a suggestion. It may call for more than some campers want to take, and should be modified to suit your individual ideas, especially if you have had some experience in camp life. It provides for a two-man party having automotive transportation; good use will be found for each item.

1 Dutch oven, cast iron, 10- or 12-inch. The handiest piece of equipment you can have; although heavy, it will cook anything, bake bread, and make stew or a pot of beans.

1 double boiler, aluminum, 2-quart. Makes two saucepans or a kettle that can be set in the ashes and left without scorching oatmeal.

1 frying pan, plain black iron, 10-inch. A cast-iron skillet is better but heavy; over an open fire, the new bright steel and stainless steel or aluminum pans will burn their contents.

1 camp coffeepot, with bail, 2-quart or larger. Tin or light steel is better than enamelware; wooden handles soon burn.

1 water bucket, galvanized, 10- or 12-quart.

1 straight-sided kettle, steel, with bail, 4-quart. For heating water and washing dishes.

1 washbasin, tin.

1 butcher knife, 10-inch; a cooking fork and cooking spoon, both with long handles, are handy.

1 pancake turner, either spatula or shovel style.

1 can opener.

1 asbestos mitt.

3-4 plates, cups, and cereal bowls. Heavy plastic ware is most satisfactory.

3-4 sets knives, forks, and teaspoons.

1-2 dish cloths or artificial sponges. Several dish towels. Wash them out before they get stiff. An oven rack from an old kitchen range is a useful addition, but will warp and buckle if it gets too hot.

With this equipment, you can cook and serve anything you may get with a minimum of trouble and confusion. Unless you have done camp cooking, you will save embarrassment and produce better results with one of the several good books on the subject that are on sale at most bookstores. Cooking in camp is much different from the outdoor cookery that you may have prided yourself on doing over a charcoal grill in the backyard, close to the kitchen and its stock of whatever is needed. In camp, you make do with what is at hand.

Provisions

As explained by the experts of the U. S. Bureau of Mines, the food taken on prospecting trips depends upon the transportation to be used and the size of the pocketbook. Plain, wholesome fare is generally preferred in camp, especially where hard work is done. If economy is involved, the food will consist mostly of dried staples and vegetables. If the supplies are to be packed on animals, bulky foods such as potatoes and many canned articles may have to be omitted. Otherwise, individual preferences should be followed as much as practicable.

A proper balance should be kept in making out a "grub list," so that needed items will not run short. It has been found by experience that fancy groceries are the ones left over and the first articles to be used are the bacon, potatoes, and flour. The standbys in prospectors' camps include flour, beans, bacon, oatmeal, dried or canned fruit, coffee, syrup for hotcakes, and sugar and canned milk for the coffee and cereal. As funds get low, more beans and less bacon are consumed, and canned fruit is omitted. Canned tomatoes are commonly used, supplying needed food elements not contained in dry staples. Where available nearby, potatoes, onions, and other vegetables are eaten. Fresh meat is not used much in camps in the summer because it is difficult to keep.

For some of these provisions, such as flour, baking powder, and shortening, substitutes may be found among the time-saving commercial products—biscuit, muffin, and pancake mixes, powdered eggs and milk, and the great variety of ready-to-cook items familiar to every modern housewife. Certain stores which specialize in sporting and camping equipment stock concentrated foods of the military-ration type.

The following weekly allowance of food for one person has been suggested to give a balanced diet:

3 1-pound cans of evaporated milk.
2 pounds of potatoes.
4 pounds of onions, cabbage, beets, or other vegetables.

3 pounds of citrus fruits, or 6 pounds of fresh apples, or the equivalent in dried prunes, apricots, etc.
3 pounds of dried beans.
6 to 8 pounds of cereals, whole-wheat flour or bread, oatmeal, shredded wheat, etc.
2½ pounds of dried meat, canned meat or fish, bacon, ham, or cheese (fresh meat or eggs may be substituted if available).
3 pounds of sugar.
1 pound of coffee.
¼ pound of salt.
small can of baking powder.

Prospecting Equipment

If prospecting and collecting are the real purpose of your trip, it is worthwhile to consider carefully what you will need, because it is difficult to develop satisfactory substitutes for this type of equipment. The list below may be revised according to how much work you intend to do. If your trip is a beginning one, to get experience, you can probably dispense with some of the items; on the other hand, if you really intend to develop a prospect, some additional things will be needed.

Maps of the area you intend to work in. Get the most detailed ones you can locate: U. S. Geological Survey, U. S. Forest Service, state maps, military, or any others. Take along a heavy pasteboard or metal mailing tube to keep them in.
1 pocket compass.
1 black iron gold pan, 16-inch. A copper-bottomed pan is of no extra value for ordinary use, but a pan with a few corrugations or riffles on the lip will help to save fine particles.
1 horseshoe magnet, large. One from an old telephone magneto is perfect; used to clean out black sand from the gold pan.
1 magnifying glass, 5- or 6-power or stronger.
1 shovel, No. 2 round point, long handle.
1 drifting pick, about 3 or 4 pounds. This type has two pointed ends and a handle fitted and wedged in like an ax. Avoid a railroad or clay pick, which is heavier, has one point and one chisel bit, and fits loosely on the handle.
1 single jack, 3 or 4 pounds. This is a short-handled striking hammer.

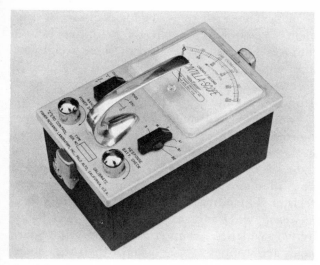

This Fisher Geiger counter is similar to most of the radioactive detectors used during the uranium rush. Portable and fairly light in weight, it is self-contained.

2-3 gads, or moils, made from ⅞-inch or 1-inch drill steel, with punch points, and ranging in length from 8 to 18 inches.

1 Geiger counter or scintillation counter.

1 tape, 50 or 100 feet. A cloth tape, cheaper and more durable than steel, is good enough for laying out claims.

a few location notices and a few empty tobacco or baking-powder cans to put them in when you place them in your location monument.

12 or more canvas sample bags. Used with a supply of cloth tags for rock samples to be assayed. A soft black pencil, which does not smear when wet, is best for filling out the tags.

Do not attempt to handle explosives, unless

This Detectron Geiger counter is a portable model having an attached probe. The signals of radioactivity are received by the probe.

Newer Geiger counters employ transistors. This one, a portable Fisher model, has a projecting probe which can reach into rock crevices.

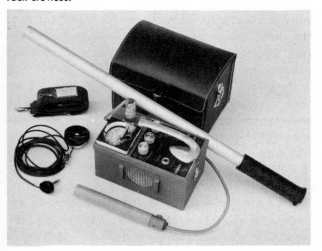

some member of the party is experienced in their use; if so, he will know what is needed in the way of drill steel, dynamite, fuse and caps, and a cap crimper. Otherwise, the above gads and single jack will enable you to get as far down in a rock outcrop as you can without powder.

When you are planning your itinerary, do not fail to make liberal allowance for the inevitable delays of weather, transportation, and possible indisposition. "Don't go into unsettled areas alone" is good advice. ("Don't go into mines of uncertain safety at all" is even better advice.) If you and your partners decide to separate for a day's reconnaissance, have a definite understanding as to which direction each is taking, the general area to be covered, and when you expect to get back to camp.

How to Use a Geiger Counter and a Scintillation Counter

The detection of uranium ores and minerals, as well as of thorium minerals, and the presence of other elements that are radioactive, has been simplified by the use of several devices—most notably the *Geiger counter* and the *scintillation counter*.

Radioactivity means that certain rays and particles are given off automatically as the elements break down by themselves and go through a whole series of changes, ending eventually as lead. During this process, heat energy and helium are also liberated. The discovery of radioactivity was made in 1896 by a French physicist, Henri Becquerel, who found that a photographic plate wrapped in lightproof black paper had been darkened by invisible radiation from a uranium compound. This simple test can be used even today, resulting in a *radioautograph*. A small metallic object—coin, key, or the like—is placed on the wrapped film, and the mineral specimen is placed on top of that. If the rock is radioactive, the image of the key or coin will show on the developed film.

Since radiation is soundless and invisible, special methods must be used to detect it. The three rays given off by uranium minerals are alpha, beta, and gamma rays. *Alpha rays,* which lose their strength very quickly (a thin sheet of paper will stop them completely), are atoms of helium that have lost their two outer electrons and are thus positively charged. *Beta rays* are similar to electrons, which are negative charges of electricity, and are therefore opposite to alpha rays. Beta rays can pass through a thin sheet of lead. *Gamma rays,* being true rays like those of light, are not electrically charged but resemble strong X-rays. They are many times more powerful, however, and can pass through eight inches of lead. It is the gamma rays that are chiefly recorded by the Geiger counter.

The Geiger Counter

Based upon the principle that radioactive emanations enable gas to conduct electricity, the Geiger counter was first developed in 1928 for use in the laboratory. This earliest device consisted of a wire surrounded by a metal cyclinder filled with low-pressure air. When first adapted to field use, it was large and clumsy, but today's counters have been perfected to the rugged, compact instruments so frequently seen in the field. Specialized counters have been developed: some weigh less than a pound, others are designed to examine boreholes, and still others enable one to prospect from an airplane.

When the Geiger counter is near a radioactive substance, the rays cause pulses of electric current in the tube. Depending upon the type of counter, these are recorded as clicks in the earphone, or are amplified as a flashing light, or cause a meter to register. The number of these pulses per minute is the *count,* which indicates the amount of radioactivity to which the counter is exposed. Alpha particles are stopped by the wall of the tube. Some beta rays enter and are recorded. Most gamma rays pass completely through the tube without effect. Perhaps one-half of 1 percent of the gamma rays enter the tube to interact with a molecule of the enclosed gas and produce electrons. These negatively charged electrons are attracted toward the positively charged wire in the center of the tube and produce a negative electrical impulse as they collect on the wire.

Certain precautions should be observed in the use and care of a Geiger counter, because it is a highly sensitive instrument. It should, of course, be turned off when not in use, to conserve the batteries. An accurate reading can be assured only by keeping it away from a watch, compass, or other instrument having a luminous dial, for the luminous paint contains a compound that is radioactive. If the needle swings to the top of the dial, or if individual clicks cannot be distinguished in the earphones, this means that the radioactive field is an intense one and the counter may be damaged. Move away from the source of the radioactivity or use a less sensitive counter setting. Protect your Geiger counter at all times from contamination by radioactive ore specimens, mine or mill dust, or radioactive clothing. Unless your counter has been sealed against moisture by the manufacturer, be sure to keep it dry, or else it may short out. This is especially true if you are working in a wet or damp mine.

The Scintillation Counter

The Geiger counter is the workhorse of the radioactive detection devices. It is sturdy and dependable and adequate for most prospecting in the field. The more recently developed scintillation counter, however, is more sensitive, as well as more expensive, and is being used increasingly to measure low levels of radioactivity, and to make general aerial surveys of terrain, in order to outline favorable places for future ground prospecting.

Whereas the Geiger counter has a vacuum

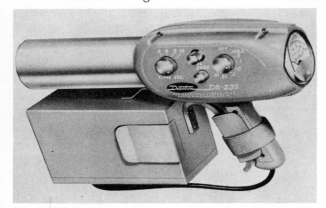

The Detectron scintillation counter records radioactivity by means of a crystal and photomultiplier tube. It is much more sensitive than a Geiger counter.

tube, the scintillation counter has a crystal called a *phosphor* and a *photomultiplier tube*. It measures beta and gamma rays, but it depends for its effect upon the ability of these rays to produce tiny scintillations (or flashes of light) in a crystal of sodium iodide or potassium iodide. This crystal is attached to the photomultiplier tube, and both crystal and tube are sealed in a light-tight unit to protect them from the sun. The tube transforms the scintillations produced in the crystal and transmits them as electrical impulses, which are amplified and passed through an averaging circuit to a recording meter.

The "Background Count" . . .

While using either type of counter, you must remember that it will record a number of small pulses even when it is not near radioactive material. This effect is due to cosmic rays and to the fact that almost everything around us is somewhat radioactive. Such normal radioactivity of our surroundings is termed the *background count*. Tunnels or mines, valleys, bodies of granite, and other features may yield a higher background count than normal. The presence of radioactive minerals causes the count to go up, and it is this increase that is actually significant.

The prospector's first job, then, is to determine the background count of the area he is exploring, by taking readings of from one to three minutes' duration (the longer time will give a more accurate reading) in various spots and at various times of day, as the background count varies both in time and place. Changes may result from a difference in cosmic radiation, weather, or the sensitivity of the counter itself. Igneous rocks are typically more radioactive than sedimentary rocks; a change in bedrock will thus result in a definite change in count as well.

. . . And How to Use the Data

Having determined the background count, the prospector should walk over the area in which he is interested, noting topography and geology. If the counter registers two or three times the background count at any place, he should stop and examine the ground more thoroughly, bringing the counter probe closer to determine the exact source of the radioactivity. Bear in mind that a relatively large area of weakly radioactive rocks will register as much count as a small crevice filled with high-grade ore. Any area that consistently gives readings of more than several times the background count should be given careful attention. Samples should certainly be taken for assay if the count registers four times that of the background count.

Do not cover the ground too rapidly; give the counter time to record narrow veins. Soil, or overburden, can conceal gamma rays; hence, readings above soil are not as accurate as those above bedrock, but soil readings can be used to gain an idea as to the possibility of radioactive rocks beneath. High-grade ore will be easier to detect than low-grade (but still profitable) ore, and even high-grade ore can rarely be detected if there is more than two feet of overburden. The presence of radon gas, thorium, and other radioactive elements can give misleadingly high counter readings. The readings will also be off if the rocks are not in equilibrium, which means that some of the uranium has been dissolved and carried away by ground water, leaving just the radioactive byproducts. Remember, also, that only a final chemical analysis will tell you how much uranium remains to be sold to the government.

The Berylometer

Related in principle to the scintillation counter, the *Berylometer* is a two-man portable instrument that unfailingly detects the presence of beryllium in any mineral or mixture. The device contains radioactive antimony, which produces gamma rays; these convert ordinary beryllium into a lighter isotope, releasing neutrons which are counted by a scintillator. The models of the Berylometer thus far manufactured are expensive, heavy, and burdensome to use, but further improvement can doubtless be expected.

How to Use a Black Light

Ultraviolet radiation is often referred to as *cold light,* because it generates little heat, and as *black light,* because it is invisible. However, it is converted into visible colors by substances that show *fluorescence.* Some of these fluorescent substances will continue to glow after the source of radiation is removed; this is called *phosphorescence.* The overall term for both reactions is *luminescence.* It can be used to advantage in prospecting and in mineral identification.

Luminescence can be produced by X-rays, cathode rays, and radioactivity, but ultraviolet sources are safer, less expensive, and more convenient. Portable ultraviolet lamps, or so-called black lights, are sold for field use.

As the invisible rays strike the atoms of luminescent minerals, they displace electrons from them. When these electrons return to their original positions, part of their newly acquired energy is released in the form of light. The invisible wavelengths are thus changed into longer, visible ones. Sir George G. Stokes named the resulting effect fluorescence, after the mineral fluorite.

Which Minerals Fluoresce?

The valuable tungsten mineral known as scheelite is one of the few minerals that always fluoresce. It greatly resembles worthless white

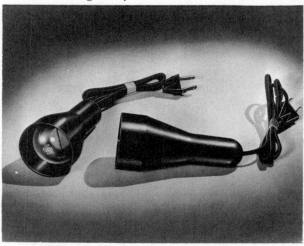

A General Electric argon bulb is a simple means of observing luminescence inexpensively. It fits into any ordinary light socket.

Scheelite is a tungsten mineral that always fluoresces under ultraviolet light. This Mineralight lamp is portable for use in the field at night.

A Mineralight shows luminescence by providing a source of ultraviolet light. A phosphorescent mineral will continue to glow after the light is turned off.

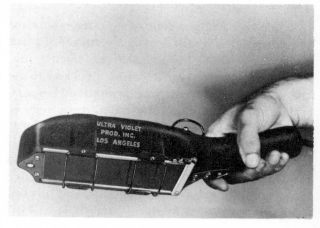

This Fisher ultraviolet lamp is a portable model for outdoor use where current is not available.

quartz, although it is unusually heavy for a non-metallic mineral. However, it can be distinguished by its blue color under ultraviolet light; this hue grades into yellow as molybdenum substitutes for some of the tungsten.

Prospecting for scheelite with a portable black light can be done in the following manner: At dusk, work uphill along parallel lines a few yards apart in a likely area, examining both soil and outcrops for traces of fluorescence. When you have located a promising area, examine fresh rock with the black light. If a favorable indication results, cut representative samples across the outcrop for future assay.

It is disappointing to record that the more valuable uranium minerals are not fluorescent. Nevertheless, some of the accompanying secondary uranium minerals (such as autunite and torbernite) do glow under the black light, and these may furnish the needed clue to the proximity of good ore. Thus, you can prospect all night as well as all day!

For examination of rocks and minerals at home, one or two inexpensive argon bulbs can be used. These do not require a filter and can be screwed into any household electrical outlet. Much more effective, however, is a mercury-vapor lamp, fitted with an appropriate filter to cut out as much visible light as possible. Some new models of the black light create both *long* and

short wavelengths of ultraviolet light, and these will bring a response from all the various kinds of luminescent minerals.

For the hobbyist, the Franklin minerals of New Jersey have a special appeal. The willemite glows bright green, and the calcite turns watermelon red. Wernerite from Ontario and Quebec gleams tawny yellow under the black light. Some diamonds are fluorescent, as is opal from the western United States. Although it has given its name to this phenomenon, fluorite seldom shows it well.

Hackmannite is the only mineral known to undergo an actual change of color due to ultraviolet light. White specimens from Ontario become pink under ultraviolet radiation, but they return to their original color when re-exposed to sunlight. Freshly broken pink hackmannite will lose its color in direct sunlight, regaining its pink hue in the dark. Another form of hackmannite turns deep violet in sunlight, though this color disappears under the light of an ordinary electric bulb.

Field Tests

As explained in the next chapter, the identification of most minerals is best left to the expe-

U. S. Geological Survey

A geochemical test is being carried out for cobalt in Idaho. Small traces may suggest that a commercial body is nearby.

rienced geologist or mineralogist, and the prospector has numerous services open to him for this purpose. Certain tests, however, are easy to perform with almost no equipment. Samples of known minerals, which can be bought from any mineral dealer, should be tested at home before trying unknown specimens in the field.

Simple Test for Tin

The only important worldwide ore of tin is cassiterite, often called tinstone or stream tin. Originating in veins and pegmatite, it is often found in placer deposits. When a piece of metallic zinc is placed next to it in a glass, and hydrochloric (muriatic) acid is added, cassiterite will become coated with gray tin. It is the only mineral that will do this. Boiling the solution and letting it stand for a while afterward is recommended. When the mineral is rinsed in water and rubbed on cloth, the metallic tin becomes shiny.

Malayan Tin Bureau

Cassiterite, an oxide of tin, is the chief tin-bearing mineral. This specimen comes from Malaya.

Simple Test for Carbonates

When moistened with hydrochloric (muriatic) acid, any carbonate mineral or rock will bubble or fizz. This *effervescence* is the escape of carbon dioxide from the substance. Calcite, limestone, dolomite, and marble react in this way, but so do carbonates of useful metals, including copper, zinc, lead, and iron. Some carbonates need to be powdered or heated in order to react favorably, but the principle is the same.

Pan-American Petroleum Corporation

Rock samples are tested with acids and other chemicals to determine their identification. This test is being carried out in British Columbia.

Prospectors, mineral collectors, and geologists test for copper, silver, and molybdenum with these supplies.

U. S. Geological Survey

Simple Test for Phosphate Rock

Although commercially valuable, ordinary phosphate rock does not have any distinctive appearance—it resembles various common and usually worthless rocks. An easy test for the phosphate content is therefore worth knowing. When nitric acid is poured on phosphate rock, and a solution of ammonium molybdate is added, the rock turns yellow. If this test is done in a glass, the mixture should be heated and then allowed to cool for several hours, if necessary, to bring down a yellow powder.

Chapter 5

HOW TO PAN
FOR GOLD

Chapter 5

HOW TO PAN FOR GOLD

The old saying that "gold is where you find it" has more application to vein, or lode, mining than it does to placers. One basic fact governs the deposit of placer gold: gold is very heavy, so that, as it is carried by water, it drops to the bottom wherever the velocity of the current is not great enough to move it along further. Any occurrence of placer gold can be explained on this basis, even though the stream may be dry at the present time. The original placer may have been in a pattern of ancient drainage that is now on top of a mountain, thousands of feet above the present streams, and possibly at right angles to the present water courses.

Where to Look for Gold

This means, for example, that if you are prospecting a running stream, you should observe the current and do your work where it is slack, not where the water is running swiftly. Drop a stick or a leaf in the current and watch its behavior. Where it slows down or eddies around will be where the gold will settle out. Other things being equal, you will have better results above a rapids than in them, and on a comparatively slow-moving stream rather than one that dashes down a steep hillside.

Eddies and potholes below sizable falls may or may not be good places to look. It is true that they form good settling basins, and therefore favorable spots for gold, but the very motion of the water keeps the sand and gravel stirred up, and thus tends to form an efficient grinding machine; any gold that might be caught is likely to be ground finer and finer until the current washes it downstream.

It is obvious that the coarser the gold, the higher the velocity of the current required to keep it in motion, so that the coarser gold will be deposited first as the current slows down—that is, toward the upper end of a slack current. If *colors* (individual particles) are present, they will become progressively smaller and smaller downstream.

In most of the western United States, the present land surface is the result of many geologic ups and downs; only rarely has the prehistoric drainage pattern been the same as it is now. Geologically recent streams have no monopoly on placer gold, so that the metal frequently is found in concentrations that have no apparent relation to the present drainage pattern.

Deposits away from water are usually spoken of as *dry placers,* and their economic value depends more on the possibility of getting the sediment to water, or water to the mineral, than it does on their assay returns. Many dry placers have been extremely rich, and much time and money has been spent in developing machines with which to work them without the aid of water, or perhaps with very limited quantities of water. These attempts in the main have been unsuccessful, but there is always the possibility that someone will come up with a practicable idea, so prospectors continue to look for dry placers.

If a stream shows fairly good colors for some distance, alternating with barren stretches where there is nothing in the character of the stream to account for them, it will usually be worthwhile to study the geology carefully. It is entirely possible that the good gravels occur where the present stream has cut across drainages of a previous geologic age, the latter being the ones that actually carry the "values." Perhaps a careful examination of the area will enable you to locate the former stream beds and their gold deposits.

When you find a few colors, or more, in your pan, work upstream to the next likely place and pan another sample. As you continue this process, the showing in your pan should improve as long as you are below the source of the gold, since, as explained, the coarser gold settles out first. Be sure to take a panful below any point where a side stream or even a dry gulch enters as a tributary.

If you suddenly find that you are not recovering the usual amount of color, you can be sure that you have gone above the source of the gold. Then it becomes a matter of sampling at closer and closer intervals until you pinpoint the location. You may find it coming in from a side drainage, in which case you will follow up that stream or gulch in the same fashion.

You may find that the gold ceases rather suddenly, without any obvious reason. When that happens, you should thoroughly investigate the slopes on both sides of the stream at that point, to see whether you can locate an outcrop of a gold-bearing vein that has fed the placer gold to the stream. In such an instance, any gold in the stream will consist of rough and irregular particles. Well-rounded smooth nuggets or very small particles of gold have most likely been carried a long distance by water; conversely, rough, irregular, and ragged fragments, thick in proportion to their surface area, indicate that the source is not too far away.

How to Get the Gold

The process of panning itself depends, for a recovery of gold, upon the same principle cited above as accounting for its deposition in the first place. The whole operation resolves itself into a problem of getting the particles of gold suspended in water so that they will have a chance to sink freely to the bottom of the pan.

The gold pan is ordinarily made of black sheet iron, sixteen inches in diameter and two and one-half inches deep, with the edges flared at about a thirty-degree angle. For special purposes, such as amalgamating with mercury, the whole pan, or sometimes just the bottom, may be of copper, but

this feature has no value in ordinary prospecting.

Smaller pans, ten or twelve inches in diameter, are frequently used for testing purposes, and in a pinch, a frying pan will do. The pan must be free of grease; a new gold pan is greasy when bought,

U. S. Geological Survey

This pan of gold nuggets is valued at $6,000. It was taken from Quartz Creek, Yukon Territory.

and it should be burned out in the fire, after which it rusts easily; but some prospectors maintain that the slightly rough rusty surface is an aid in saving fine colors.

A pool of slack water, six or more inches deep, is the ideal place to pan, as there is enough current to carry away the fine particles which make the water muddy. A good-sized washtub is satisfactory, if water is scarce or you are not yet confident of your ability and want to save what might otherwise go down the stream.

The first step is to fill the gold pan to the brim, or perhaps a little heaped up, with the gravel to be tested. In taking a sample from the stream, dig down as far as possible under the water, discarding the gravel that is at the immediate bottom of the stream, because it will be so thoroughly washed as to be barren. The farther down toward bedrock you take the sample, the better chance you will have of finding gold in it.

Submerge the pan in the water, and break up with your hands all the lumps of dirt, stirring the gravel meanwhile. You will perhaps find it most comfortable to kneel on one knee, or sit on your haunches while handling the pan. Keep working the contents of the pan under water until all of the fine material, silt, and clay have been washed away, and only clean gravel, sand, and pebbles remain. Pick out any pebbles larger than a pea and discard them. If they should be of any value, their weight will cause you to examine them more closely.

The bulk of the material in the pan will now have been reduced to a small fraction of what it was originally. Holding the pan under water, rock it gently in a circular motion, dropping first one wrist slightly, then the other, until you get the mass of gravel moving in a circular movement around the pan. Now, while continuing the rotary motion, drop the far edge slightly; you will find that you can thus make the gravel climb up the sloping side of the pan and spill over the edge. Work off most of the largest particles, which will be the ones nearest the edge; then tilt the pan back and return the whole mass to the bottom of the pan, and repeat the process.

As you continue, the amount of material decreases, and the particles left in the pan become progressively smaller. When you get down to a tablespoonful or so, or perhaps long before, you will almost invariably find a considerable quan-

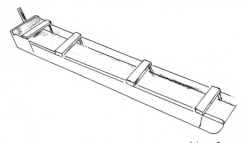

Arizona Bureau of Mines

The recovery of gold from sand and gravel is the purpose of a sluice box. Many kinds of sluice boxes can be constructed from simple materials.

tity of *black sand*—this is largely magnetite, which, as its name implies, is attracted to a magnet. It is heavier than ordinary sand or gravel, but lighter than gold, and it is the practically universal companion of placer gold. Its presence is certainly no guarantee that placer gold is also present, but its absence is almost certain evidence of the absence of gold, too. It also is a help in judging your progress in panning, for if you can save the black sand, you are certainly not losing the gold, which is much heavier than black sand and therefore less likely to be washed away.

Keep up the manipulations, using care that you do not spill material over the edge too vigorously. With even a tablespoonful, and surely with

less, you can gently rotate the pan as before and make the material string out in a long slender half moon, in the angle between the bottom and the side of the pan. At the leading edge (in the direction of movement), there will probably be some light-colored sand which is mostly quartz; behind that will be the black sand; and, if you are fortunate to find any, at the tail end of the half moon will be the grains of gold. They may range in size

Arizona Bureau of Mines

A rocker is another device for taking gold fom placer material. The name "cradle" is also used. The heavy gold settles out of the sediment.

from colors smaller (usually much smaller) than the head of a pin and very thin, to grains somewhat larger; if you are one of the lucky ones to find coarse gold, it will range in size from a grain of wheat or smaller to perhaps the size of a pea.

Colors, unless there are a great many of them, are of no real value except as an indication of the presence of gold in the gravel. Larger particles indicate a much more valuable find. The average color that can be saved by not-too-skillful panning averages about one-tenth of a cent to the pan. That is, thirty colors means that the panful of dirt contains only about three cents worth of gold. Each pan of gravel weighs more than twenty pounds. A good man who works eight or ten hours a day in cold water will pan between one-half or two-thirds of a yard of gravel. In exceptionally clean gravel, he might pan a cubic yard. Obviously, under present economic conditions, a gold pan is a prospecting aid and not a production tool.

The amateur prospector can reassure himself with this fact: it is almost impossible, with any care at all, not to save particles of gold that are large enough to be of any consequence. The fine colors can get away, but anything as big as a mustard seed is pretty likely to resist efforts to wash it aside. The only time that saving fine colors is really important is when gravel is sampled to determine its worth and whether it will justify an operation on a larger scale.

Having reduced the panful to the smallest quantity, rinse it into a can or bottle. At the end of the day, you can pan the whole accumulation again—this will be mostly black sand—and reduce the quantity as much as possible by slow panning. Then dry the residue over a fire. You can blow most of the black sand away, by working carefully, or you can remove most of it, when thoroughly dry, with a magnet.

When using a magnet, place a piece of paper or thin cloth between the magnet and the black sand. The sand will adhere to the paper. After taking it from the pan, pull the paper away from the magnet, and the black sand will fall off. Without a paper or cloth, it will be hard to remove the black sand from the poles of the magnet.

Chapter 6

WHAT DO YOU HAVE—
AND HOW MUCH?

Chapter 6

WHAT DO YOU HAVE— AND HOW MUCH?

The time comes when every collector and amateur prospector finds indications of what he hopes may be a commercial mineral deposit. Two questions must then be answered: First, is it what he thinks it is—for the best of us get fooled on occasion. Second, is there enough of it to justify spending time and money on it?

The first question calls for *identification*, or *qualitative determination*—that is, "What is it?" or "What does it contain?" The second question calls for *quantitative determination* or *assay*—that is, "How much of it is there?"

Determining the Name

Problems of identification range from the simplest specimen—such as a perfect cube of pyrite, which any tyro should be able to recognize at sight—to the most complex aggregate of rare earths, requiring optical, X-ray, or other special techniques. Using one of the standard books that give instructions on how to know the minerals and rocks (see Chapter 12), the beginner can gradually increase his ability to make satisfactory identifications in the field, bringing home the more troublesome specimens to examine in the laboratory or to send away for professional assistance.

How the Identification Is Made

The use of the blowpipe is described later in this book (Chapter 8). Even many men who are well qualified to make their own tests have abandoned the practice, however, preferring to send almost all their likely specimens to one of the many laboratories that handle identifications. One compelling reason for doing so is that the day of the old-time prospector, his interest centered on the metallic ores of gold, silver, lead, and copper, has gone. Many of the minerals that are most in demand now do not lend themselves to the simple tests that can be made without a well-equipped laboratory.

There is, perhaps, one outstanding exception to that statement—the radioactive elements. These substances cause a Geiger counter or scintillation counter to react readily, and the intensity of the response gives some indication of the amount of radioactive elements that may be present. Even for this class of material, however, it is necessary to turn to laboratory methods to make a positive identification of just which elements are present— to distinguish between uranium and thorium, for example, and to determine the percentages.

In the laboratory, many different techniques and types of equipment are employed. A routine chemical qualitative analysis is normally a rather simple operation in a well-furnished laboratory, but it has largely given way to other means, such as microscopic, spectroscopic, and X-ray examinations.

The sulfide ores and other opaque minerals may be mounted in a plastic medium, polished on a revolving wheel, and examined with a *metallographic microscope*. In addition to identifying the minerals that are seen, it is usually possible to determine whether the grains are large or small, well separated or intergrown, how much grinding would be necessary to liberate them, and other information about the physical state of the sample, all of which is of interest to both miner and metallurgist.

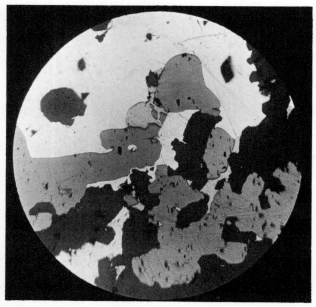

U. S. Geological Survey

Ore specimens are ground flat and given a high polish for study under the reflecting microscope. Each mineral has its own color, shape, and other properties.

This metallographic microscope by Bausch & Lomb is used to examine polished sections of ores by reflected light.

The transparent minerals are examined with a *petrographic microscope* as crushed grains on a glass slide or by preparing thin sections. The minerals are identified and evaluated by their various optical properties.

Spectroscopic investigations are carried out with highly specialized optical instruments, and they reveal the chemical elements in the sample.

When solid or powdered minerals are exposed to an *X-ray beam,* and the rays that are diffracted from the atoms are recorded and measured, it is possible to identify the minerals and distinguish between those having the same chemical composition but different structures.

Where Your Specimens Can be Identified

Almost all the states of the Union, and certainly all the states in which mineral deposits are or have been important, maintain agencies that will make identifications free of charge for their residents, or on materials originating within the state. Usually, these agencies are connected with the state educational institutions, such as the state university or school of mines, or else with the state geological survey, bureau of mines, or similar department.

Approximately one-half of the states have institutions of higher education that give degrees in mining or metallurgical engineering. In some cases, they are special schools, such as the Michigan College of Mines and Technology, at Houghton; in others, they are departments of the state university, such as the Mackay School of Mines of the University of Nevada, at Reno. Every state has one or more colleges or universities that give courses in geology. Almost any of these institutions will make simple identifications without charge, and if any charge is made for more complicated work, it will usually be only nominal. If in doubt, the easiest solution might be to write to the state university and ask where you can have an identification made.

Another source of such information is the U. S. Bureau of Mines, Washington 25, D. C. Although it attempts to avoid duplication of services rendered by state bureaus, this federal agency will identify samples as far as can be done by inspection and perform optical and qualitative chemical tests. Such examination is usually sufficient to indicate whether the material has commercial value, or at least if the expense of a private assay would be warranted. Advice is also given as to possible markets.

Specimens submitted to the U. S. Bureau of Mines should be addressed to one of the following stations.

Southern Experiment Station: U. S. Bureau of Mines, Tuscaloosa, Alabama.

Southwestern Experiment Station: U. S. Bureau of Mines, Tucson, Arizona.

Denver Experiment Station: U. S. Bureau of Mines, Denver, Colorado.

North Central Experiment Station: U. S. Bureau of Mines, College Park, Maryland.

Mississippi Valley Experiment Station: U. S. Bureau of Mines, Rolla, Missouri.

Rare and Precious Minerals Experiment Station: U. S. Bureau of Mines, Reno, Nevada.

Rapid City Experiment Station: U. S. Bureau of Mines, Rapid City, South Dakota.

Intermountain Experiment Station: U. S. Bureau of Mines, Salt Lake City, Utah.

Division of Mineral Technology, Field Office: U. S. Bureau of Mines, Spokane, Washington.

Uranium and thorium samples may also be sent for free examination to the U. S. Geological Survey, Geochemistry and Petrology Branch, Building 213, Naval Gun Factory, Washington 25, D. C.

In Canada, the Department of Mines and Resources, Ottawa, identifies Canadian minerals free of charge and makes certain assays and analyses for a fee. The laboratories of the provincial governments also are available for these services.

In Mexico, the address of the Government Laboratory is Unidad Experimental de Tecamacholco de la Comisión de Fomento Minero, Loma de Chapultepec, Apartado Postal 10505, México, D. F. No charge is made for identifications.

Even for identification, no school or government agency can be expected to compete with commercial firms that do such work as a business. An occasional sample or a few at a time will be accepted, but if you send in a long series of specimens, especially if there appears to be a commer-

Socony Mobil Oil Company

Isolated deposits of rock are being sampled in the Northwest Territories, Canada.

A sandstone outcrop near Warren, Montana, is being sampled for study purposes.

Standard Oil Company, New Jersey

cial operation involved, you will doubtless be referred to a private company.

It is always wise to explain the reason for your inquiry, in order to get a prompt reply and possibly to avoid disappointment. Asking "What is the pink color due to?" or "Does this rock carry titanium?" or "Does this sample contain rare earths, and if so, which ones?" indicates that you have some reason for asking other than mere curiosity.

Determining the Amount

After the identification of a commercially useful mineral deposit, the next step is to take a representative sample for assay or quantitative analysis. *Sampling,* the procedure of securing a small portion of a deposit which will truly represent the value of the whole, is a difficult thing, at best, but of much importance. One of the greatest obstacles to securing a representative sample is the personality of the prospector. If he is an optimist by nature—and most prospectors distinctly are—he will unconsciously select the better appearing pieces to represent the whole, and the result will give an exaggerated idea of the quality of his "strike." Conversely, a pessimist will strive so hard to avoid being misled that he will probably include too many low-grade pieces of rock and will fall short of an average value.

For that reason, certain more or less arbitrary methods of selecting samples are necessary. These will increase the accuracy of the sample, but even with them, it is essential to maintain a strictly objective attitude.

The Grab Sample

A *grab sample,* consisting of pieces selected at random from an outcrop or pile of rock such as a

Rock is being examined in the field. The location is The Llanos, Colombia.

Standard Oil Company, New Jersey

dump, is usually worthless. However, if the prospector will pick up any piece of rock without selection but at regular intervals along a straight line across an outcrop, or from the bottom to the top of a dump, he will take some of the personal element out of the sampling procedure. Even then, there are so many variables in the nature of earth substances that no more than a general idea can be expected from this method. The ore may be harder or softer than the waste rock, so that the valuable pieces will be larger or smaller than the average. It may be heavier, so that the lower portion of the pile will be the valuable part—and still other conditions may exist.

The Chip Sample

Another method, better than that of garnering a grab sample but still not too satisfactory, is to knock off chips with a prospecting pick or chisel at regular intervals all across the exposure, until enough is secured for a sample. The more different the pieces that are included, the more nearly correct will be the result. Here, again, the characteristics of the valuable material affect the results. If it breaks off in larger or smaller pieces than the average, the sample will be off correspondingly.

The Channel Sample

The best method for the prospector to use is to take a *channel sample.* First, the sample interval is marked out along the vein, using the flame of a carbide lamp or a timber-marking crayon. The area on the vein to be sampled should be cleaned off by chipping away the outer layer of vein material. The channel should then be marked out from three to six inches wide and one inch deep underground, although on the surface the channel may be wider and deeper. The ore should be chipped out across the entire width of the vein with a pick, hammer and moil, drill, or prospector's pick—maintaining a constant width and depth of the channel throughout. Care should be taken not to break off too much soft material, because it tends to average higher in value than the rest. A sheet of canvas will collect the fine cuttings, especially when one is working on an almost vertical wall, and these are likely to be the most valuable part of the sample. A powder box is often used to catch the chips from the channel, after which the chips

Standard Oil Company, New Jersey

Rock sampling is being conducted in the field for evidence of mineralization.

Diamond core drilling is the most effective way to penetrate the earth. The diamonds are the industrial variety, not gem stones.

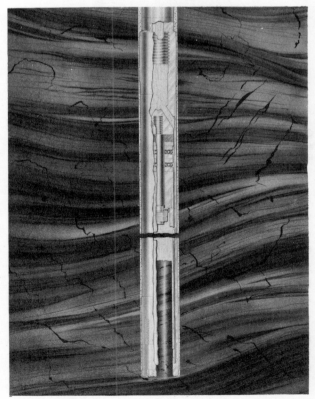

E. J. Longyear Company

and cuttings are put in a strong cloth sack, with a slip inside giving its number. It is also good practice to tie a tag with the number and your name on the outside of the sack.

Cores

Drill cores are often taken in sampling. They have the advantage that they can be studied intact, revealing the original rock relationships.

How to Process Your Sample

It is essential to keep a list of the samples as they are taken, recording the numbers assigned, where they came from, and any pertinent comments. A rough sketch map showing the source of the samples may prove desirable for future reference.

E. J. Longyear Company

Only by use of a drilling bit can the actual condition of buried rock be determined. Scientific instruments merely give indications that may not be borne out by the visible evidence.

A sample secured by any of the above methods may be too large to handle conveniently or to ship to the assayer or laboratory. One or two pounds is usually the right amount to submit. To reduce the bulk of a sample, crush it to as nearly a uniform fineness as practicable, usually with no piece larger than about one-half inch in any dimension —the smaller the particles, the better, as long as they are reasonably uniform in size. Lacking power equipment, the best tool is a large iron mortar and pestle, such as can be obtained from any store carrying mining or laboratory equipment.

The preferred method of cutting the size of a sample is by the use of a *sample splitter,* of which there are two principal types. One of these, the *Jones riffle,* is too bulky for field use. It consists of a hopper above a series of open-bottom pockets, usually one-half or three-fourths inch wide, which are so constructed as to discharge alternately, first into a pan to the right, and then into another pan to the left. Each time the sample is passed through the riffle, it is divided into two equal parts; the next pass of one of those parts will give a quarter of the original sample, and so on, until the sample is reduced to the desired weight. For best results, it is well to go through the operation until a sample of the correct size is obtained, and then combine all the fractions and repeat the process. A variant of the Jones riffle, often called a *hand sampler,* consists of a gridiron of heavy tin plate, with troughs one-half or three-fourths inch wide alternating with openings of the same width.

Another method, commonly spoken of as *cone sampling,* is reasonably accurate and particularly adapted to very large samples. The smaller the quantity to be reduced, the finer the sample should be crushed. Upon a flat surface, such as a piece of sheet iron or heavy linoleum or a tight wooden floor, the sample is shoveled into a cone-shaped pile. It is then spread out in a flat bed two or three inches deep, and then shoveled into a cone again, with care being taken to deposit each shovelful on the apex of the cone. The more times, within reason, that this shoveling is repeated, the better mixed and therefore more representative the small sample will be, provided all the material is worked each time, especially the fine sizes. As a last step, the material is again flattened out into a circular

North American Philips Company

X-ray diffraction equipment photographs the atomic pattern in minerals. Each crystalline mineral produces a different pattern.

pile and divided, like a pie, into four quarters. The opposite quarters are saved, repiled, flattened, and again quartered. Each time the process of quartering is repeated, the bulk of the sample is reduced by one-half.

It is always good practice to keep a duplicate of each sample you submit for analysis, at least until you have received the returns from the laboratory. It might be necessary to duplicate the test for some reason, or you might question the results of a sin-

Braun-Knecht-Heimann

The Jones sample splitter is standard equipment for dividing crushed rock into equal portions. Half of each sample goes through each side of the box.

gle test and wish to have it done again by some other method.

How the Determination Is Made

Having secured a series of representative samples, the next step is to have them analyzed or assayed, in order to determine whether there is enough of the desired mineral present to make it worthwhile to continue development. The usual means of securing that information is by one of many regular chemical analyses, referred to as *wet tests*.

For gold, silver, and platinum, the *fire assay* is used. This process consists of fusing the sample in an assay furnace, using lead oxide and a reducing agent in a crucible. The precious metals are collected in the lead. The mass of lead is then removed by oxidation and absorption in bone ash, leaving a bead of metal to be weighed. The proportion of gold and silver will be determined by another step.

The technique of *spectrographic analysis* consists of producing, recording, and measuring the optical emission spectra of the chemical elements in

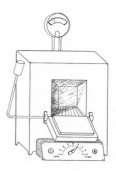

Braun-Knecht-Heimann

An assayer's furnace is employed for the fire-assay method. This decides the amount of gold, silver, or platinum in a sample.

samples, using highly specialized equipment. Each element has its own emission spectra in the visible and ultraviolet wavelength regions usually used. Infrared spectra, both emission and absorption, and fluorescent X-ray emission spectra are also employed. It has been stated that, with emission spectrographs, as little as one part of metal in a million parts of rock can be detected.

Several methods of analysis based upon measurements of radioactivity are now being utilized successfully. Accurate measurements of the natural radioactivity of mineral and ore samples are a means of determining their content of uranium, thorium, radium, potassium, and other elements.

As emphasized previously, the government and educational institutions are not in rivalry with private firms in making quantitative determina-

Braun-Knecht-Heimann

The assayer's balance is especially designed for fire assaying and chemical analysis. It gives highly accurate results when carefully used.

tions. Any of the places where identifications are made will undoubtedly refer you to commercial firms in your area upon request; also, the mining magazines carry advertisements of laboratories that do this sort of work.

Prices vary greatly, both by geographic region and according to the particular elements or minerals involved. It is always wise to secure a price list or estimate before sending samples in for a quantitative determination, or you may be in for a real shock if you are interested in platinum or certain other difficult substances. If you have a large number of samples, or a number to be run for the same kind of test, you will probably get a reduced price, especially if you secure a quotation before sending in the samples.

U. S. Bureau of Mines Information Circular 7695 (available on request from any Bureau of Mines office) has a list of commercial laboratories throughout the United States. In Alaska, the Department of Mines (under the office of the Commissioner of Mines) operates four assay offices. Assays and analyses are made without charge to Alaskan prospectors and to mining companies engaged in mine development. Operating companies are charged at commercial rates.

Mine Development

Early consideration should be given to certain economic aspects of your claim. No deposit, regardless of its size or quality, is of immediate value if it is so inaccessible that it cannot be mined and its minerals processed, transported, and sold at a profit in a competitive market.

The material from many mines requires some concentration or cleaning to remove impurities. This treatment is commonly called *beneficiation*. Concentration reduces the bulk and improves the grade of a mineral product to save on costs of transportation and treatment. Some companies having the necessary equipment and experience make small-scale beneficiation tests on lots of ore weighing from fifty pounds to a ton or so. From the results of such tests, the most suitable method of handling can be determined, and enough of the finished product can be obtained to submit as trial samples to possible consumers.

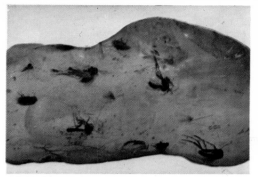

AMBER
(enclosing insects)
Baltic

AMETHYST
San Eugenio, Uruguay

AQUAMARINE CRYSTALS
Minas Gerais, Brazil

ARAGONITE CRYSTALS
Cumberland, England

ARAGONITE and SULFUR
Cianciana, Sicily

BARITE
Fort Morgan, Colorado

BARITE
Badlands, South Dakota

CALCITE CRYSTALS
Stark Mine, Lancashire, England

CHRYSOBERYL TWIN CRYSTALS
Lake Alaotra, Madagascar

CHRYSOCOLLA
Globe, Arizona

CROCOITE
Near Dundas, Tasmania

ERYTHRITE
Sonora, Mexico

HEMATITE
(iron rose variety)
Saint Gothard, Switzerland

JASPER CABOCHONS
Egypt

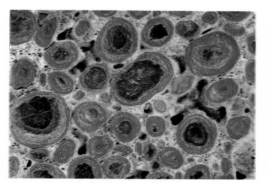

LIMONITE (pisolitic)
Tern Island, New Zealand

MALACHITE and AZURITE
Bisbee, Arizona

MALACHITE CABOCHONS
Congo

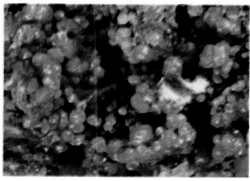

MIMETITE and HEMIMORPHITE
Cumberland, England

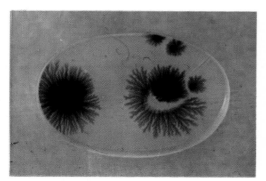

MOSS AGATE
Wyoming

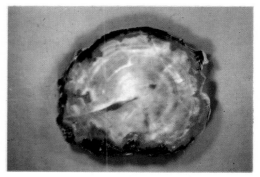

PETRIFIED WOOD
Holbrook, Arizona

PRECIOUS OPAL (inside)
Nevada

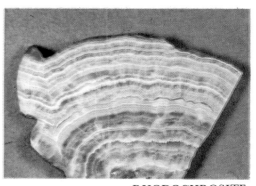

RHODOCHROSITE
Catamarca Province, Argentina

RUBELLITE
(a variety of tourmaline)
Pala, California

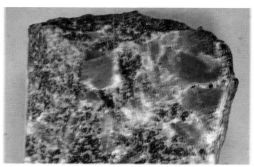

RUBY CORUNDUM
Clay County, North Carolina

SILVER CRYSTALS
(after cleaning)
Houghton County, Michigan

SAPPHIRES
(a variety of corundum)
Ceylon

TOPAZ CRYSTALS
(enclosing quartz)
Thomas Range, Utah

TOURMALINE
California

URANOPILITE with JOHANNITE
and GUMMITE
Near Hite, Utah

URANOPILITE and ZIPPEITE
on PITCHBLENDE
Happy Jack Mine,
San Juan County, Utah

WULFENITE and MIMETITE
Chihuaha, Mexico

ZIRCON CRYSTALS (blue)
Thailand

Chapter 7

STAKING A
MINING CLAIM

Chapter 7

STAKING A MINING CLAIM

It is only one step from finding a mineral deposit of potential value to acquiring the mineral rights necessary for commercial exploitation of the claim.

The whole subject of mineral rights is covered by what is usually referred to as *mining law*. It is, from its very nature, a complicated study, and it varies according to the ownership of the land in question. This brief discussion is an attempt to present the major facets of the problem in a general way, and to indicate where further information may be obtained. Nothing written here is to be construed as anything more than general guidance, and it should be understood that if you have a specific question of law, a qualified attorney should be consulted.

Development of the Mining Law

The basic law under which title to government land valuable for mineral deposits may be obtained is the Congressional Act of May 10, 1872, with amendments. In effect, this law set forth in legal form the procedures that were developed by trial and error in the mining camps of the West, notably the gold camps of California and the silver mines of the Comstock Lode in Nevada.

There are two basic concepts. The first is that of *fissure veins,* or *lodes,* of mineral-bearing material. These are presumed to stand more or less vertically, extend downward indefinitely, and be confined between rather well-defined walls of non-mineral material called *country rock.* On the surface, their direction is rather constant and subject to being determined.

The second concept of the mining law is that of *placers*—alluvial deposits carrying free gold distributed through them, and lying in more or less horizontal planes. The broad distinction is between mineral "in place," that is, in veins in solid rock, and placer gold, which has been set free by erosion from its enclosing rock and then transported elsewhere by water.

What the Original Law Specified

Theoretically, a prospector could discover the outcrop, or *apex* of a lode, and would be entitled to claim a portion of it—finally decided as 1,500 feet —along the length of the lode on the surface of the ground, and to follow it down toward the center of the earth as far as he could, or wished to. Such a lode claim eventually developed into a tract of land that could be not more than 1,500 feet in length and not more than 600 feet in width.

The only other requirement of the basic law was that the *endlines,* which theoretically crossed the lode at right angles, must be parallel, and that the *sidelines* could not at any point be more than 300 feet from the center of the vein or lode along its course.

Aside from these two restrictions, the law of 1872 said no more. The sidelines could be in any position or any shape, and there was no requirement that they be parallel, although they could not infringe upon a prior valid claim.

Because the principle was that of a claim 1,500 feet long, the claimant obviously could not work beyond his endlines, since to do so would give him more than 1,500 feet. There were, however, no such restrictions about crossing the sidelines, and because veins are seldom vertical, a claim owner was, in theory at least, entitled to follow a vein to China if he wanted to, through his neighbor's ground on the side toward which the vein dipped, so long as he did not cross his own endlines or their extension.

The trouble is that the lodes or veins do not follow the ideal pattern that the lawmakers had in mind. They widen, pinch out, disappear, reappear, intersect others, split, join with other veins, change their characteristics with depth, outcrop or apex in more than one place, and generally play hob with everybody but the lawyers and the mining engineers. Many of these professional men grew rich from the litigation that plagued any successful mining operation in the early days.

Placers are not so complicated, at least as far as gold deposits are concerned. Up to twenty acres could be claimed by an individual, and an association of up to eight individuals could claim twenty acres for each person involved; such a 160-acre plot was considered as one claim, and only one discovery and one *assessment work* (improvement work) required for it.

Mineral Leasing Act of 1920

The situation remained generally unchanged for about fifty years, until the passage of the Mineral Leasing Act of February 25, 1920, which removed certain minerals from acquisition under the mining law, and provided for the leasing of their deposits. This law affected the following mineral resources: coal, oil, gas, oil shale, sodium, phosphate, and potash, and in Louisiana and New Mexico, sulfur. Those minerals can be acquired only under the mineral leasing laws and are not subject to location under the United States mining laws.

The Atomic Age Affects Mining Law

The atomic age produced another change in the laws, when the discovery and exploitation of uranium became of vital importance to national defense. It happened that vast tracts of land in the areas that were becoming important for uranium had previously been leased under the 1920 law, and therefore were not open to prospecting and development of uranium and kindred minerals. These lands were, under certain conditions, thrown open to prospectors and locators for uranium after World War II.

Mining Law Today—the New Approach

The latest change in federal law represents a logical outgrowth of the philosophy that brought about the leasing law of 1920, and is embodied in the Congressional Act of July 23, 1955. In essence, it represents the belief that natural resources, both mineral and vegetable, on the unappropriated public domain should be kept as the property of all the people rather than passing into private ownership—the principle, in other words, that is broadly spoken of as conservation of natural resources. Under this principle, the national forests, as an example, are administered to get the most good for all the people out of the timber, the forage, the water, and the recreational opportunities available on them, rather than to allow these lands to pass into private ownership and thus beyond the reach of the public generally.

One of the major problems in such multiple-use administration of the national forests and other similar government land has been the loopholes that existed in the mining laws, notably the possibility of locating and securing full ownership (*patenting*) of claims on the strength of the existence of such widely distributed deposits as gravel, sand, and building stone, all of which were formerly claimable as valuable minerals under the law. This resulted in many claims being perfected, and even patented, for such uses as summer homes, fishing lodges, and tourist resorts, under the guise of mining claims.

The law of 1955 applies to public lands administered by the Department of Agriculture and the Bureau of Land Management; it does not apply to lands in any national park or monument or to any Indian lands. It provides that, on claims filed after that date, the miner may use his claim for prospecting, mining, or processing operations and the uses reasonably incident to them, but not for any other purposes, prior to patent. This means that he has the right to use timber for mining purposes on his claim, and that he can also remove timber to provide clearance, but that he cannot use the claim for a summer home, for instance, or cut the timber to sell. Neither can he use it to graze stock not used in connection with his mining operations, nor lease it to others for grazing purposes. Until the miner obtains a patent, the United States can manage and dispose of the surface resources, such as timber and grass, and manage other surface resources, such as springs and streams, provided that such disposal or management does not endanger or materially interfere with the miner's prospecting, mining, or processing operations. The intent is to protect the public interest as well as that of the prospector or miner.

Furthermore, and very importantly, claims can no longer be located on the basis of the discovery of common varieties of sand, stone, gravel, pumice, pumicite, and cinders. This does not preclude valid claims based on discoveries of uncommon minerals such as gold that occur in such ordinary deposits. It does stop most of the people who formerly made use of the mining laws to acquire land for purposes other than mining.

Status of Land

Your first step will be to ascertain by inquiry of the proper county official (usually the county assessor or his equivalent) whether the land in which you are interested is *private land,* is *state land* (land belonging to the state in which it lies), or is *government land* (that is, owned by the United States).

Private Land

If the deposit is found to be on private land, the arrangements will have to be made entirely with the landowner, or with the actual holder of the *mineral rights* to the property. Thus, it becomes a question of negotiation between the parties concerned.

State Land

If the land is state-owned, further procedure will be in accordance with the laws of the particular state. Such procedures vary greatly from one state to another, and are subject to change from time to time. The only safe thing to do is to write to the state agency having charge of such matters, give the location of the land you have in mind, and ask for the latest information on how to proceed. The only other person whose advice you should heed is an attorney. Don't depend on amateur advice.

There is given below a list of the state agencies charged with supervision of state land in each of the states. The form of your request does not matter, as long as you specifically identify the land and give enough other information to permit an intelligent reply.

Alabama	Secretary of State, Montgomery
Alaska	Director, Division of Lands, Department of Natural Resources, Anchorage
Arizona	State Land Commissioner, Phoenix
Arkansas	Commissioner of State Lands, Little Rock
California	Division of State Lands, Sacramento
Colorado	State Board of Land Commissioners, Denver
Connecticut	The State Treasurer, Hartford
Delaware	Chairman, State Park Commission, Dover
Florida	Commissioner of Agriculture, Tallahassee
Georgia	Secretary of State, Atlanta
Hawaii	Department of Public Lands, State Office Building, Honolulu
Idaho	State Land Commissioner, Boise
Illinois	Auditor of Public Accounts, Springfield
Indiana	Auditor of State, Indianapolis
Iowa	Secretary of State, Des Moines
Kansas	Auditor of State & Register of State Lands, Topeka
Kentucky	Commissioner of Finance, Dept. of Finance, Frankfort, regarding land sales; Secretary of State, Frankfort, regarding old land records.
Louisiana	Register, State Land Office, Baton Rouge
Maine	State Land Agent and Forest Commissioner, State House, Augusta
Maryland	Land Commissioner, Annapolis
Massachusetts	Department of Conservation, State House, Boston
Michigan	Auditor General, Tax Division, State Capitol Building, Lansing

Minnesota	Director, Division of Lands & Minerals, St. Paul
Mississippi	Land Commissioner, Jackson
Missouri	Secretary of State, Jefferson City
Montana	Commissioner of State Lands & Investments, Helena
Nebraska	Board of Educational Lands and Funds, Lincoln
Nevada	State Land Register, Carson City
New Hampshire	State Forester, Concord
New Jersey	Department of Conservation and Economic Development, Trenton
New Mexico	Commissioner of Public Lands, Santa Fe
New York	Board of Commissioners of Land Office, Albany, regarding forest lands; Director of Lands and Forests, c/o Conservation Department, Albany
North Carolina	Secretary of State, Raleigh
North Dakota	State Land Commissioner, Bismarck
Ohio	Auditor of State, Columbus
Oklahoma	Secretary, Commissioner of the Land Office, Oklahoma City
Oregon	Clerk of State Land Board, Salem
Pennsylvania	Secretary of Internal Affairs, Harrisburg
Rhode Island	No State Land
South Carolina	Secretary, Sinking Fund Commission, Columbia
South Dakota	Commissioner of School and Public Lands, Pierre
Tennessee	State Property Administration, Nashville
Texas	Commissioner, General Land Office, Austin
Utah	Executive Secretary, State Land Board, Salt Lake City
Virginia	State Librarian, Virginia State Library, Richmond
Vermont	State Forester, Montpelier
Washington	Commissioner, Department of Public Lands, Olympia
West Virginia	State Tax Commissioner, or State Auditor, Charleston
Wisconsin	The Commissioners of the Public Lands, Madison
Wyoming	Commissioner of Public Lands, Cheyenne

NORTH AMERICA

Canada	Northern Administration & Lands Branch, Department of Northern Affairs & National Resources, Ottawa, Canada
Mexico	Secretary of Agriculture, Mexico City, Mexico
Panama	Secretary of the Treasury, Panama, Republic of Panama
Puerto Rico	Office of Puerto Rico, 2210 R Street, N.W., Washington D.C.
Virgin Islands	Governor, St. Thomas, Virgin Islands, U.S.A.

Government Land

If your investigation discloses that the land in which you are interested is the property of the United States, usually referred to as government land, or *public domain,* there are many points to be considered before you can arrive at a correct procedure. The one place where the authoritative answer may be obtained is the Bureau of Land Management, Department of Interior, Washington 25, D. C. An inquiry addressed there will be referred to the proper office, and eventually you will get a reply. That reply, however, will probably be confusing to you unless you have some basic information to start with, and this is the purpose of the discussion here.

First, consider some of the special cases which may arise. If the area in which you are interested lies either in a national forest or in a national park or monument, the simplest and easiest way to find out just what you can do about locating a claim is to ask the nearest ranger. He can either tell you himself or get the information for you. In most cases, locations cannot be made in national parks or national monuments, but national-forest land is open to prospecting and location under established procedures.

Prospecting and mining permits on Indian reservations are usually handled by the tribal council of the tribe concerned, but the best place to secure preliminary information is from the Bureau of Indian Affairs, Department of the Interior, Washington 25, D. C.

The nearest office of the Bureau of Land Management can tell you whether the land you are interested in is within any of the above-mentioned special areas, if you cannot find out locally, or whether it has been withdrawn by such agencies as the military establishments, the Bureau of Reclamation, or the Federal Power Commission. It is absolutely necessary to give the exact location of the land you are asking about, by *legal description* if it has been surveyed.

Offices of the Bureau of Land Management are located as follows:

Regional Administrators

Federal Building (P.O. Box 480), Anchorage, Alaska

630 Sansome Street, San Francisco 11, California

1245 North 29th Street, Billings, Montana

1015 West Tijeras Avenue, N.W. (P.O. Box 1695), Albuquerque, New Mexico

1 Swan Island Station, Portland 18, Oregon

238 Federal Building, Salt Lake City, Utah

Land Offices

Federal Building (P.O. Box 1740), Anchorage, Alaska

Post Office Building (Box 110), Fairbanks, Alaska

1512 Post Office Building, Los Angeles, California

352 New Federal Building, Sacramento, California

1245 North 29th Street, Billings, Montana

1 Swan Island Station, Portland 18, Oregon

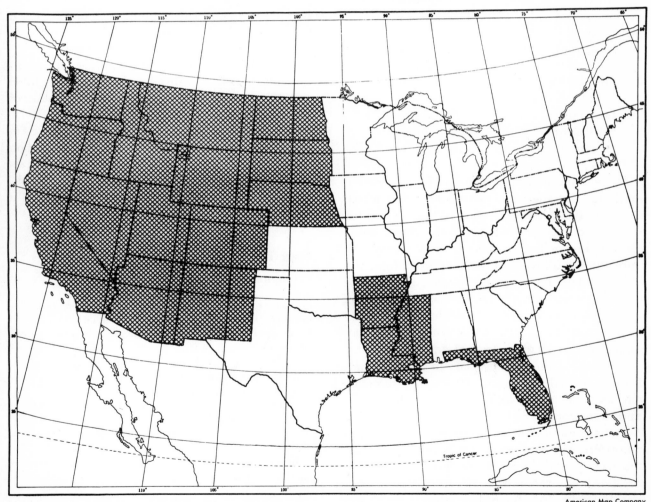

American Map Company

The shaded states above, and Alaska, are the so-called public land states, to which the basic mining law of land claims applies.

Land and Survey Offices

251 Post Office Building, Phoenix, Arizona

437 Post Office Building, Denver, Colorado

Box 2237 Boise, Idaho

322 Post Office Building, Reno, Nevada

P.O. Box 1251, Santa Fe, New Mexico

209 Federal Building, Spokane, Washington

313 Federal Building, Salt Lake City, Utah

405 Federal Building (Box 578), Cheyenne, Wyoming

Public-Land States

The original mining law of 1872, as amended, applies to vacant government land in the following nineteen *public-land states* (if it does not come under any of the special cases mentioned in the preceding paragraphs or in other reservations).

Alaska	Nebraska
Arkansas	Nevada
Arizona	New Mexico
California	North Dakota
Colorado	Oregon
Florida	South Dakota
Idaho	Utah
Louisiana	Washington
Mississippi	Wyoming
Montana	

This act and its amendments and supplemental legislation are the basic provisions under which all rights to mineral deposits in vacant United States land may be acquired in the above states. No state law or local custom of miners may give more than is allowed under federal statute; but such local laws may, and often have, limited these rights by prescribing the number or size of claims, by placing added burdens upon locators, and by setting up detailed rules for carrying out the general requirements of the federal statutes.

For that reason, it is necessary to secure the additional special regulations for each state before you can make a valid location. Most of the public-land states, especially in the mining regions of the West, have met this need by publishing pamphlets containing all the necessary general information and setting forth in detail the federal, as well as the state, requirements. It is suggested that your first step, when you have found that the land you have in mind is government land, should be to ask the agency in your particular state for a copy of such publication.

Making the Location

There are four essential elements in locating either lode or placer claims: (1) discovery of mineral, (2) marking the boundaries, (3) posting the notice of location, and (4) recording an exact copy of the notice.

All that the federal statutes require, after a discovery of mineral, is that the location be distinctly marked on the ground so that its boundaries can be readily traced; also, all records of mining claims must contain: (1) the name or names of the locators; (2) the date of the location; and (3) a description of the claim or claims (located by reference to some natural object or permanent monument), so that the property can be identified. Further rules and any amplification of the federal requirements are left up to each state, as long as they are not in conflict with the basic law.

Approved forms of location notices are available at stores in any mining area; properly filled out, they will usually satisfy the requirements of the local laws; their use is advised.

There are no restrictions in the federal law as to the number of claims an individual or association of individuals may locate. Citizenship is not required of the locator, but a patent cannot be obtained by an alien, and an adverse claim of a citizen will hold over that of an alien.

State Laws

Colorado, for instance, requires that

the discoverer of a lode, within three months from the date of discovery, shall record his claim in the office of the recorder of the county in which such lode is situated, by a location certificate which shall contain:

1. The name of the lode.
2. The name of the locator.
3. The date of location.
4. The number of feet in length claimed on each side of the discovery shaft.
5. The general course of the lode as near as may be.

Before filing such location certificate the discoverer shall locate his claim by:

1. Sinking a discovery shaft upon the lode to the depth of at least ten feet from the lowest part of the rim of such shaft at

the surface, or deeper, if necessary to show a well-defined crevice. [This has now been modified, as discussed later.]

2. By posting at the point of discovery on the surface a plain sign or notice, containing the name of the lode, the name of the locator, and date of discovery.

3. By marking the surface boundaries of the claim. Such surface boundaries shall be marked by six substantial posts—one at each corner and one at the center of each side-line.

In California, as an example of state variations, the six posts are required to be at the corners and at the middle of the endlines, instead of the side-lines, as in Colorado. Again, in California the discoverer has ninety days in which to sink his discovery shaft, while in Colorado he is allowed sixty days.

Until quite recently, a legal discovery of a valuable mineral was held in all the states to mean the actual physical finding of useful mineral material, and the exposing of it to view, so that a prudent man would be justified in spending time or money

NOTICE OF LODE LOCATION

———

NAME OF LODE

_____

NAME OF LOCATOR

_____

DATE OF LOCATION

_____

_____19_____

Out West Printing and Stationery Company

in developing it. For a lode claim, the mineral must have been "in place," that is, where it originally occurred in the solid rock and not broken loose and moved somewhere else—as would be the case with fragments of ore called *float*, scattered around on the surface of the ground. For a placer claim, it was sufficient to be able to prove its existence within the boundaries of the claim.

As a direct outgrowth of technical advances and the increasing importance of radioactive minerals, a radical change is developing in the requirements for a "discovery" of a valuable mineral. The development of geophysical methods of pros-

pecting, such as the Geiger counter, together with core drilling, makes it possible to prove, or at least to be confident of, the existence of deposits of uranium and similar minerals beneath the surface of the earth, without ever seeing them exposed. These deposits, although locatable as lode claims, rarely conform to the original concept of a lode.

STATE OF COLORADO,
County of..................... } ss.

KNOW ALL MEN BY THESE PRESENTS, That.............., the undersigned, ha........this ....day of......................., 19........, located and claimed, and by these presents do......locate and claim by right of discovery and location, in compliance with the Mining Acts of Congress, approved May 10, 1872, and all subsequent acts, and with local customs, laws and regulations,.....................linear feet and horizontal measurement on the.............................lode, vein, ledge or deposit, along the vein thereof, with all its dips, angles and variations as allowed by law, together with ....feet on the.....................side and.................... feet on the......................side of the middle of said vein at the surface, so far as can be determined from present developments; and all veins, lodes, ledges, or deposits and surface ground within the lines of said claim.....................feet running ....from center of discovery.....................and ....feet running.....................from center of discovery....................., said discovery.....................being situate upon said lode, vein, ledge or deposit, and within the lines of said claim in..................... ....Mining District, County of..................... and State of Colorado.

Discovered and located....................., 19........

....
....
....

Out West Printing and Stationery Company

A lode location notice, required for vein deposits of minerals.

A lode location notice, required for vein deposits of minerals.

A lode location notice, required for vein deposits of minerals.

Notice to all Persons is hereby given, That..........................

....

did on the.....................day of.....................19........, discover and disclose a lode bearing valuable..................... minerals, and ha........developed and defined said lode.....................and named it ....LODE; and did on the ....day of.....................19........, claim and locate upon the ground.....................hundred..................... linear feet in length of the said...Lode, with...feet in width of surface ground,.....................linear feet of said lode so located being..................... ....of the center of discovery.........................thereon, and..................... linear feet being.........................of the center of said.....................; and ....feet in width of said surface being on the.....................side of the middle of the vein and.....................feet being on the.....................side thereof.

Said claim is situated in...Mining District, in the County of.........................and State of Colorado, and the boundaries thereof are as follows, to-wit:

Out West Printing and Stationery Company

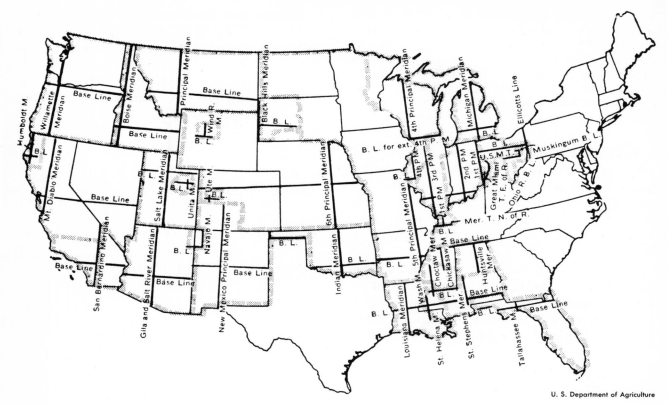

U. S. Department of Agriculture

Location of the several prime meridians and their base lines.

New Mexico, as an example of the current thinking in this respect, accepts a drill hole as a substitute for the discovery shaft, tunnel, or pit, provided that a deposit of valuable mineral is intersected. Colorado has taken another approach by substituting, for the requirement of a discovery shaft, the map of a survey made on a scale of 500 feet to the inch and attached to the location certificate when it is recorded in the office of the county clerk; a valid discovery of mineral must nevertheless be made on the claim.

These brief examples should demonstrate the absolute necessity of becoming familiar with the regulations of the particular state in which you are working, or of securing the services of a competent engineer or attorney to advise you.

Placer Claims

The requirements for a placer claim are simpler in both the federal and state laws than those for a lode claim. A placer claim cannot exceed twenty acres for an individual claimant, but up to eight individuals may band together and locate one placer claim of a maximum of 160 acres (twenty acres for each person in the group). The advantage

is that only one discovery of mineral is necessary for the entire claim, whether of twenty or 160 acres, as well as only one discovery shaft and one annual assessment.

Placer claims should, where possible, conform to legal subdivisions (*sections*); if they are in a surveyed township, they are required to do so. In an unsurveyed township, their boundaries should run toward the four main points of the compass; they should be as nearly square as possible. In either surveyed or unsurveyed townships, the smallest legal subdivision recognized is ten acres. This last rule is to avoid "shoestrings" along creeks, for example, whereby one claim might take up miles of potential placer ground along a drainage if a minimum width were not prescribed. (A square ten-acre tract is 660 feet on each side.)

The federal statute does not prescribe marking on the ground for placer claims corresponding to legal subdivisions, and it is sometimes not necessary, the theory being that the surveyor's section corners will serve the purpose. It is, however, desirable to mark the corners of any placer with substantial posts, and in Colorado and some other states, this is required.

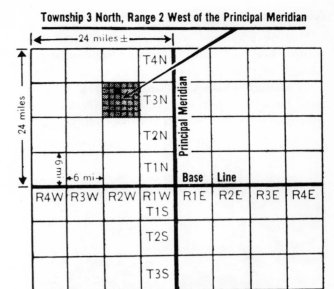

Township 3 North, Range 2 West of the Principal Meridian

U. S. Department of Agriculture

Dividing an area into townships.

Section 9. Township 3 North, Range 2 West of
the Principal Meridian

6	5	4	3	2	1
7	8	9	10	11	12
18	17	16	15	14	13
19	20	21	22	23	24
30	29	28	27	26	25
31	32	33	34	35	36

1 mile

1 mile

Sections 1 through 6 on the north side and 7, 18, 19, 30, and
31 on the west side are fractional sections.

U. S. Department of Agriculture

A township divided into sections.

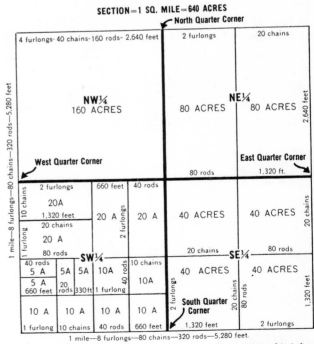

SECTION=1 SQ. MILE=640 ACRES

U. S. Department of Agriculture

Section of land showing acreage and distances.

Assessment Work

Having complied with the federal and state mining laws, a locator is entitled to possession of his lode or placer claim as long as he does his annual assessment work or "annual labor" on it, or until he secures patent to it. The federal law requires at least $100 worth of work each year; the

Standard Oil Company, New Jersey

The use of the plane table and alidade for surveying mineral claims is shown. The scene is the Big Horn Mountains, Wyoming.

state statutes vary in their detailed specifications of what this work must consist of and the exact period within which it must be done. If a number of contiguous claims are held in common, the entire amount of assessment work, at the rate of $100 for each claim, may be done on any one of the group if it benefits the rest. Under certain state provisions, work done off the claim or group, such as road construction to enable access to the property, may fulfill the requirement.

Other kinds of claims are allowable under the mining laws—mill sites and tunnel claims, for instance—but they are beyond the scope of this discussion. Information concerning them will ordinarily be contained in the publications available from the departments concerned in each individual state.

Patents

A valid location, followed by annual assessment work as required, is sufficient to hold a mining claim indefinitely, under present laws, but it confers only a temporary right. If actual ownership is desired, a definite procedure is set up to enable the claimant to secure a patent, the equivalent of a deed, from the United States.

This involves: (1) a survey (in the case of all lode claims and some placers) by a United States mineral surveyor; (2) proof of expenditure of $500 on each claim; (3) publication of various legal notices; and (4) the eventual payment to the government of $2.50 per acre for the land. This payment, incidentally, is by far the least part of the cost of patent proceedings.

The details of patenting can be obtained from the Bureau of Land Management. A patent is not necessary at any time for the continuation of the mining uses of a claim, which can be leased, sold, and willed to heirs in the same way as ordinary property. After a patent is obtained, however, the owner can use it for anything he wishes, but he must then also pay taxes on it. Numerous large producing mines did not go to patent for years, and some of them have always operated under the original location rights.

Chapter 8

THE COLLECTOR
AT HOME

Chapter 8

THE COLLECTOR
AT HOME

Once you have gathered rock and mineral specimens in the field, the second and equally enjoyable part of mineral collecting begins. The exact identification of a rock or mineral, the preparing of rough field specimens for display, and the many additional ways in which you can enjoy your mineral finds now open up before you. Mineral collecting in all its phases is an absorbing and delightful hobby, and one that often proves profitable to the rockhound who learns how to identify valuable mineral deposits by the presence of certain mineral and rock associations.

In Your Laboratory

The mineral collector soon finds it desirable to set up some sort of laboratory, however simple, where he can work with his specimens. It may be a table in one corner of the basement, a section of your den, a large closet, or even an entire room if facilities allow and your interest so dictates. Simple tests and experiments can be carried on in very little space and with only a few tools.

How to Test Hardness

Hardness has a special meaning for the mineral collector—it is the resistance which the smooth surface of a mineral offers to being scratched. This scratch-hardness is the kind of hardness by which minerals are identified; the resistance that the atoms of a specimen offer to being separated in other ways is called *toughness* or *tenacity*. A diamond, for example, is the hardest of all substances because only another diamond will scratch it, and

yet a sharp blow will cause it to split along definite planes of weakness.

More than a century ago, a German mineralogist, Friedrich Mohs, devised a handy scale of hardness which is still used. Known as *Mohs' scale,* it does not indicate exact hardness, but means only that any mineral can scratch all those beneath it in the scale and will, in turn, be scratched by those above it.

10	Diamond	5	Apatite
9	Corundum	4	Fluorite
8	Topaz	3	Calcite
7	Quartz	2	Gypsum
6	Feldspar	1	Talc

For example, a mineral with the hardness of 7 (quartz) is a little harder than feldspar and a little less hard than topaz. Quartz is often considered as marking the division between the hard and soft minerals. With a little practice, the mineral collector can familiarize himself with the use of a set of these ten minerals, known as *hardness points;* they help to make mineral identification easier. A note of warning: Do not scratch a mineral, especially a crystal, indiscriminately, or you may ruin its appearance. Make as small a scratch as possible in a place where it will show the least. It is preferable, of course, that a fine crystal or a cut gem be identified by other means.

Certain familiar objects can be used for quick identification of a specimen. A fingernail has the hardness of $2\frac{1}{2}$; a copper coin, 3; a knife blade or a piece of window glass, $5\frac{1}{2}$; and a steel file, $6\frac{1}{2}$. Minerals under $2\frac{1}{2}$ will leave a mark on paper, while those under $5\frac{1}{2}$ can be scratched by a knife. Those over $5\frac{1}{2}$ will scratch glass. Be sure to distinguish between a real scratch on a smooth surface of the mineral and the mere crushing of a rough surface by the knife edge. Also, do not mistake a white mark left by a soft mineral on the glass for a scratch. Such a mark can be rubbed off; a true scratch is permanent. Always make sure you are testing a fresh, unaltered surface.

A mineral with the hardness of 1 will have a soft, greasy feel, like talc or graphite. Number 2 can be scratched quite easily with the fingernail. Calcite, with a hardness of 3, can be scratched with a copper coin. Fluorite, hardness 4, can be scratched with a knife. Minerals with a hardness of 7 or more are few, but they include most of the gem minerals.

Kinds of Tenacity

Not to be confused with hardness is *tenacity*. Minerals have been grouped under certain types of physical resistance for further ease in identification. If a mineral will bend, only to spring back into shape when released, it is termed *elastic*. Mica is a good example of this. A mineral that breaks or powders easily, such as quartz, is called *brittle*. Talc, which can be bent out of shape and will remain bent after the pressure is removed, is *flexible*. A few minerals, notably cerargyrite and certain other silver minerals, are *sectile*—that is, they can be cut into shavings with a knife. Native copper and native silver, which can be drawn out into wire, are called *ductile*. These minerals, as well as native gold, are also *malleable*, for they can be pounded out into thin sheets.

How to Test Heaviness

Because minerals vary so greatly in weight, some being light for their size and others heavy, they can be identified by their relative density, known as *specific gravity*. Specific gravity is based on the principle of Archimedes that, when a solid body is put in water, the water displaced weighs as much as the solid body itself loses in weight by being submerged. The specific gravity of a mineral, rock, or gem is determined by making two weighings—one in air, the second in water. The formula may be expressed by stating that the spe-

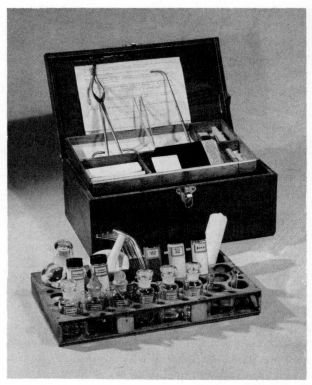

Ward's Natural Science Establishment

Laboratory kits for mineral identification can be bought from dealers, or they can be assembled at home.

cific gravity of a mineral is the weight of the specimen in air divided by the loss of weight when it is suspended in water. If a mineral weighs eight ounces in air and six in water, the difference is two ounces. Divide the original figure of eight by this difference to arrive at a specific gravity of exactly 4.00.

The specific gravity of a mineral can thus be defined as its weight divided by the weight of an equal volume of water. The specific gravity of pyrite, for example, is about 5; of sulfur, about 2—which means that these minerals are, respectively, five and two times as dense as water.

Minerals can, of course, be readily classified at sight as either metallic or nonmetallic. The average mineral with a metallic luster has a specific gravity of a little over 5—hematite, for example. If the density is 4 or less, as with graphite, the mineral will seem light in weight. If it is as high as 7 or more, as with galena, the mineral will seem heavy. Nonmetallic minerals of average density range from 2.6 to 2.8 and include quartz, calcite, and feldspar. Nonmetallic minerals vary from those of low density, having a specific gravity of less than 2.5—such as the zeolite minerals—to those of high density, having a specific gravity of 3.5 or more—such as all the lead minerals (cerussite, anglesite, pyromorphite, etc.). Diamond, topaz, zircon, and cassiterite are also of high density, cassiterite having a specific gravity of 7.

To determine specific gravity in the home laboratory, several systems can be used. Homemade equipment is perfectly adequate for most purposes. A *beam balance,* using weights distributed along a horizontal arm, can be constructed easily and is perhaps the simplest to use. The *Jolly balance,* often used by professional mineralogists, is a spring balance attached to the top of a vertical scale; two pans hang from the brass spring, the lower pan being immersed in water. The mineral or rock to be weighed is placed first in the upper pan, then in the second. The original weight, divided by the difference in the two weights, determines the specific gravity. *Heavy liquids,* such as pure bromoform with a specific gravity of 2.89, can be used to identify gems. Topaz, for example, sinks in bromoform, while yellow quartz, which resembles it, does not.

What Color and Luster Tell You

The color of a mineral is due to its chemical composition, as well as to the presence of chemical impurities within a given specimen, and even to slight variations in the usual structure. Radioactivity, which distorts the position of the atoms, has been found to be responsible for the color of some

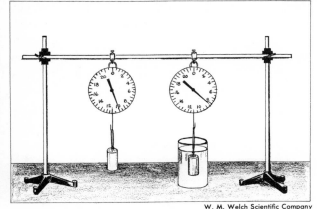

W. M. Welch Scientific Company

Here is proof of Archimedes' historic experiment in specific gravity. The specimen weighs less in water than in air. The difference in weight is proportional to the specific gravity.

minerals—that is, they owe their original color to radioactivity. Other minerals have been changed from their original color by the presence of radioactive substances. The unusual blue of some halite is due to this radiation, as is the smoky color of smoky quartz. Uranium or thorium minerals are always to be found—although not necessarily in commercial amounts—where smoky quartz is present.

Because minerals are so variable, color alone cannot be used as a sure means of identification. Quartz, for example, exists in almost every color imaginable. In general, those minerals possessing a *nonmetallic* luster vary much more in color than do those with a *metallic* luster. (Metallic refers to a mineral that is opaque and has a reflecting surface like that of a coin.)

There are a variety of nonmetallic lusters. *Vitreous* (or glassy) is perhaps the most common—this is the quality of quartz. *Adamantine* refers to the brilliant luster shown by hard, nonmetallic minerals such as corundum and diamond. A *resinous* luster, as is observed in sphalerite, resembles the resin from trees. Some specimens of milky quartz are seen to have a *greasy* luster. Fibrous minerals, such as satinspar gypsum, present a *silky* luster. The many minerals that have good cleavage and are easily split apart, such as mica, display a *pearly* luster on the broken surfaces.

Of the nonmetallic minerals, few are constant in color—sulfur is yellow; rhodonite, red; azurite, blue; and malachite, green. More often, however, a great difference in color occurs within a single species. Corundum, for instance, may be red, which we call ruby; blue corundum is called sapphire.

Variations in the appearance of metallic minerals are most commonly due to a slight surface change, chiefly *tarnish.* This outward coating is sometimes dull, sometimes bright. Pyrite, brass yellow in color, becomes quite dark when tarnished. Most notable, probably, is the change in bornite ("peacock ore"), a copper-iron sulfide which in its original state is a reddish bronze, but which upon exposure to the air tarnishes rapidly, becoming a variegated blue and purple and turning almost completely black in a short while. To be more sure of the real color, you should break the mineral open in order to obtain a fresh surface.

Most minerals, when crushed, lose their color entirely. Some will show a color similar to that of the original specimen, only paler; others will yield a bright color, which may even be a different color from the original solid specimen. This color of the powdered mineral is referred to as its *streak,* since

Eberbach & Sons

With the Jolly balance the specific gravity can be calculated by the amount that the spring stretches. The specimen is weighed first in air, than in water.

it is obtained by rubbing the mineral specimen upon a piece of unglazed white porcelain—a regular *streak plate* or the broken edge of a cup. Most nonmetallic minerals show only a white streak, even if the specimen is dark, but for many metallic minerals, the streak is extremely helpful in making an identification. In outward appearance, hematite can be reddish brown, brownish black, and even jet black in color, but when it is tested by rubbing upon a streak plate, the resulting powder will always be "Indian red," so called because the American Indians made their vivid red war paint from crushed hematite. In fact, the name of this mineral means bloodstone.

The Blowpipe Tests

When all the means previously mentioned for identifying a mineral leave you still in doubt as to the exact nature of a specimen, a simple blowpipe

test may give you a *qualitative analysis* that will enable you to make a positive identification. Such an analysis will show you what elements are present in the mineral, but not their relative amounts. (A *quantitative analysis,* as described in Chapter 6, requires a skilled chemist.) Blowpipe tests include chemical and physical tests using various chemical reagents and a few inexpensive pieces of equipment, of which the blowpipe itself is distinctive.

A blowpipe can be simple or elaborate, but as long as it has an air chamber to collect the condensed moisture from your breath, an expensive one is not necessary. A cheap blowpipe, together with a bunsen burner, an alcohol lamp, or even a candle to supply the heat, will do the job. A blowpipe is simply a metal tube used to force a narrow jet of air into a flame. This requires a little practice, as you must learn to blow out through your mouth while breathing in through your nose to maintain a continuous, steady flame. Once you learn to hold a constant supply of air in your cheeks, the rest is easy to do.

The blowpipe should be placed close to, or just within, the flame from the bunsen burner, slanting downward a little. When you blow through the tube, the blast of air from the pipe will create a horizontal, cone-shaped flame consisting of three zones. The inner zone of unburned gas mixed with air is blue in color; the middle zone of burning gas, moisture, and carbon monoxide is a pale violet shade; while the hot outer part of the flame, which consists of air, moisture, and carbon dioxide, is invisible. The middle is termed the *reducing* flame, because the carbon monoxide will "reduce" the oxygen in a mineral placed within it, even removing oxygen from heated minerals. The outer zone is called the *oxidizing flame,* because it contains an excess of oxygen from the surrounding air and will give off oxygen or oxidize a mineral

Cornelius S. Hurlbut, Jr.

Left: Charcoal block with antimony oxide coating. Right: blowpipe flame, showing component parts: a) oxidizing flame; b) reducing flame; c) unburned gases.

placed within it. This means, then, that to blow a strong oxidizing flame, the tip of the blowpipe should go just inside the gas flame, and the mineral being tested should be held so that it does not touch the inner blue cone. To make use of the reducing flame, the tip of the blowpipe should be held slightly outside the flame, and the mineral held within the blue cone, being surrounded by the yellow flame.

Before testing a mineral, it should already have been identified as nearly as possible according to metallic or nonmetallic luster, color, hardness, and specific gravity.

Any mineral known to contain silver, gold, copper, tin, or lead can be further tested by heating a fragment of the mineral on a flat piece of charcoal. By means of the reducing flame of the blowpipe, the mineral will be melted, oxygen and other volatiles will be extracted, and the metal itself will appear as a white ball of silver or tin, a yellow ball of gold, a red mass of copper, or a gray lump of lead. If iron, nickel, or cobalt should also be present in the specimen, the resulting product will be magnetic. Other elements and some metals tested in the same way will vaporize, and then settle onto the charcoal as *sublimates* (coatings) in varying positions and colors. For example, lead minerals, which for the most part are easily reduced, will leave a little ball of lead. There will also be a sublimate—yellow near the assay, white farther away. Bismuth will also leave a similar coating, but when a mixture of potassium iodide and sulfur is added, it will turn bright red. The lead sublimate, on the other hand, will turn canary yellow.

By using forceps or platinum wire, a mineral can be heated in the flame. It can then be identified either by its fusibility, or the color that it imparts to the flame, or both.

Certain chemical elements are revealed by their coloration in the flame. Strontium glows crimson, calcium turns a yellowish red, and sodium in even the smallest quantities gives off a vivid yellow. Barium has a yellow-green tint in the flame, while copper turns bright blue or emerald green. One element can often disguise the color of another element, if both are present in a specimen; so vivid is the yellow of sodium that it will prevent the pale violet of potassium being seen except through a piece of blue glass. The green of boron may not be visible unless a drop of sulfuric acid is placed on

the mineral before heating, and certain other treatments may be required for special minerals.

The *fusibility* (or melting point) of a mineral also helps to identify a specimen. A scale of fusibility for easy reference consists of the following minerals:

1. Stibnite—even large fragments melt in an ordinary flame.
2. Natrolite—fine needles fuse in an ordinary flame, larger fragments in a blowpipe flame.
3. Almandite—thin splinters will fuse in a blowpipe flame.
4. Actinolite—thin splinters will fuse to a globule in a blowpipe flame.
5. Orthoclase—thin edges will round in a blowpipe flame.
6. Bronzite—the finest edges will fuse in a blowpipe flame, but with difficulty.

Calcite, sphalerite, graphite, quartz, and topaz are among the minerals that will not fuse. Like Mohs' scale of hardness, this scale of fusibility is also somewhat variable, according to the given specimen.

A length of platinum wire fused in the end of a glass tube will make flame tests and bead tests possible. The flame of a burner, or a small lump of white powder, turns color when certain metals are added.

Other characteristics of minerals often revealed in flame tests include the curling or swelling of stilbite when subjected to heat, the bubbling and fusing of the zeolite minerals, the swelling and opening out into leaves of vermiculite, and the bright glowing without melting that is typical of calcite.

Borax melted in a loop at the end of a platinum wire, which has been inserted at the opposite end in a glass rod or other holder, can be used to make *bead tests* of powdered minerals. When a tiny bit of the powdered mineral is picked up in the hot borax bead and fused in it, the bead turns a characteristic color, depending upon the amount of powder and the type of flame—whether oxidizing or reducing. The color will change, also, when the bead cools. Varying color combinations help to identify the mineral: for example, cobalt minerals are deep blue, chromium minerals are clear green, etc. Other fluxes besides borax are used occasionally for special bead tests.

Hollow glass rods are used in making blowpipe tests of minerals that give off a volatile substance when heated. *Open-tube tests* are made with the flame, so that a continual stream of hot air passes up the tube and over the heated mineral fragment. Sulfur, or a sulfide containing a high percentage of sulfur, turns to sulfur dioxide in an open tube; this colorless gas is readily recognized by its pungent odor, and it will change dampened blue litmus paper to a red color when the paper is held at the upper end of the tube. In a *closed-tube test,* which is made in a glass rod melted shut at one end, the mineral fragment experiences a chemical reaction without being affected by oxygen. Sulfur tested in a closed tube will deposit a red sublimate which turns yellow as it cools. Other elements and compounds have their own reactions to open- and closed-tube tests.

How to Test with Chemicals

Acids and other reagents can be used to identify the elements of which minerals are composed. Hydrochloric acid, nitric acid, and sulfuric acid are most commonly used, especially the first. Nitric acid is used to determine the solubility of metallic sulfides and heavy metals such as silver, lead, and copper. The carbonate minerals effervesce in acid, giving off carbon dioxide, which is the same effect (and the same gas) seen in a carbonated drink. Such chemical tests can distinguish between two minerals that greatly resemble each other except for their individual chemical reactions; for example, calcite and aragonite will dissolve rapidly in cool acid, even in lumps, whereas dolomite and siderite, which resemble them, do not, but must be pulverized or the acid must be heated. Acid tests should be made with care, for the fumes are dangerous and will act corrosively upon nearby brass surfaces.

Enjoying Your Mineral Finds

Having identified the mineral specimens by yourself or with assistance, it is time to prepare them for permanent display. This involves trimming and cleaning them, lacquering those that need it, and providing special protection for other minerals as required. You may wish to learn how to cut and polish the gem stones in your collection. Growing one's own crystals has proved an exciting hobby for many, while thousands of rockhounds attest to the additional pleasure provided by joining a mineral society.

How to Clean Your Specimens

Once you have acquired mineral specimens for your collection, you should give some thought to their appearance and care. A clean mineral is not only more attractive, but it will retain its original characteristics longer. To have a collection of which you are proud, as much care should be given to cleaning and preserving your specimens as is spent in obtaining them. Minerals are constantly undergoing change, even in the seemingly unvarying atmosphere of a display cabinet.

Minerals react to their environment, wherever they may be. Feldspar weathers to clay; meteorites tend to crumble into powder or to decompose, even in museum collections. Of the major chemical classes of minerals, the sulfides are the least stable, the oxides the most stable. Secondary minerals are not so apt to change and so are less likely to trouble the collector.

The first step in preserving a mineral specimen is to clean it, taking every precaution not to scratch or damage it in the process. Minerals should not be cleaned or even handled too often, for they are subject to physical and chemical changes when repeatedly washed or brushed. Once cleaned, they should be kept in closed cabinets made as dust-proof as possible. Ordinary dust and soot are more of a nuisance than really harmful, except in the case of delicate filiform (hairlike) or capillary (needlelike) crystals, which are too fragile to be cleaned. These may be dusted by blowing upon them, either with the breath or with a mechanical hand blower like that used by window dressers. Such a controlled blast of air should remove linty or earthy dust from a specimen. Some fibrous crystals can be washed by carefully dipping them in alcohol, while those more strongly built can be washed in a gentle stream of water and dried in the sun. Minerals that often have a delicate structure include cuprite, malachite, the so-called feather ores, and the zeolites.

Porous and earthy minerals will absorb water or other liquids, and on drying will crack and be destroyed. These minerals, which include various kinds of clay, should be cleaned only by brushing. A soft, camel's-hair brush will remove dust; a stiff, quill brush or a wire brush can be used to remove a stained or dirty surface from a specimen.

Those minerals that are partly or entirely soluble must not be moistened, although they can be dusted with a soft brush. Some specimens can be washed in dry-cleaning fluid, as referred to later. There are a good many soluble minerals, two of the most common being borax and halite. Minerals that oxidize when moistened, as certain sulfides, can be cleaned with a soft brush.

Insoluble minerals are quite simple to clean, as they can be washed in water and rubbed with a soft brush or artificial sponge. Soapy water can be used for more stubborn specimens. Beware of strong soaps, which may cause a chemical reaction due to the presence of alkali, or gritty or abrasive soaps, which may scratch. Some soaps are fluorescent, too, which may be confusing if a specimen not thoroughly rinsed is later studied under ultraviolet light. Detergents are the best and simplest to use, since they leave no soapy film and do not cause a precipitate in water. Alabaster and marble can usually be cleaned simply by soaking them in plain water; deeply soiled pieces can be washed with soapy water to which a little ammonia may be added, and then rubbed with a soft brush or artificial sponge. Gold is one of the few minerals that does not corrode, so it does not often need cleaning, but soap is best when a specimen requires it. A dilute solution of hydrochloric acid or a 10 percent solution of ammonia can also be used to clean gold.

When a mineral is soluble in water, some other liquid in which it is insoluble may be used to clean it. The selection of a liquid depends upon the mineral—any large standard textbook on mineralogy or the table of properties in a chemistry handbook can be referred to in order to determine a mineral's solubility in various liquids. Dry-cleaning fluids—including gasoline, benzene, special petroleum solvents, and chlorinated hydrocarbons such as carbon tetrachloride—are often used. Care should be taken to guard against the danger of fire or the toxic effects of vapors.

Mineral specimens are frequently disfigured by *rust*—various ferrous and ferric iron oxides that coat the mineral with red, yellow, brown, or black deposits. Such coatings are often difficult to remove, or can be removed only by processes that take a long time. The simplest method makes use of oxalic acid, which cannot, however, be applied to minerals affected by weak acids, especially the carbonates. To employ it on suitable minerals, dissolve half an ounce of oxalic-acid crystals in a gallon of water, preferably distilled. Place the specimen to be cleaned in an aluminum pan used only for this purpose. Cover the specimen with the oxalic-acid solution. Allow the pan to boil slowly on the stove or a hot plate until the coating is dissolved. This depends on the amount of iron oxide on the specimen. Half an hour may be sufficient for some specimens, while for others the process may have to be repeated several times. A specimen that is not too delicate may be scrubbed with a brush in the cooled acid solution to remove any rust that has been softened but not dissolved by boiling. Wash the specimen in soapy water, brush it carefully, rinse it in cold water to remove all traces of the acid, and dry it.

A common chemical reaction involving the taking up of oxygen into the chemical compound of a substance is called *oxidation*. Oxidation of iron is rusting, as mentioned, but other individual minerals also undergo oxidation. Pyrite can be particularly troublesome to the collector, as air and dampness cause iron sulfide to oxidize to various iron sulfates, producing free sulfuric acid and liberating hydrogen sulfide. This reaction is a rapid one if the specimen is fractured, and the sulfuric acid turns display labels brown and brittle and may damage the wood cabinet. The hydrogen sulfide blackens any brass fittings and tarnishes other sulfide minerals. While not all pyrite is subject to rapid decomposition, oxidation must always be guarded against. It can be removed with the same oxalic-acid solution used for rust, with the warning that frequent washing will cause pyrite to oxidize more quickly than ever.

Marcasite, having the same chemical composition as pyrite, is also subject to oxidation, although not all specimens are equally susceptible. Since washing hastens its oxidation, resulting in the formation of melanterite, dry brushing is actually the only safe way to clean a specimen of marcasite. Another method involves warm oxalic acid of any strength. Using a long bristle brush, apply the acid gently to the mineral, rinse it in boiling water, and set the specimen aside to dry. The heat of the water is absorbed by the mineral, causing it to dry before reoxidation can tarnish it again.

Meteorites gradually disintegrate from the effects of oxidation, which apparently occurs during atmospheric flight as well as from the results of weathering. Stony meteorites contain less metal to undergo oxidation; a high nickel content in metallic meteorites also aids stability. It is believed that the crust of iron oxide which forms on the surface of a meteorite helps to prevent further oxidation. Few meteorites are free of it, the most common form being limonite (hydrous iron oxide), which forms a brownish black crust, penetrating more or less into the mass. Various methods for its removal are possible, including oxalic acid.

Tarnish is also caused by oxidation or, in some cases, the effect of light on certain minerals. Native copper and silver are commonly subject to tarnish. On specimens of copper, the black incrustation is due to cupric oxide, which is in the form of the mineral tenorite. The green color that is most familiar is hydrous copper carbonate, or the mineral malachite. On bronze or copper artwork, it is called *patina* and is considered a valuable addition. To the mineral collector, it is normally a nuisance which he wishes to remove. Acid usually etches and damages copper, sometimes turning it rosy red. Ammonia can result in eventual disintegration. Rough specimens of copper can be soaked in a weak solution of acetic acid. Mix one part of glacial acetic acid, which is almost pure acetic acid, with ten parts of water, soak the specimen in this solution, rinse it thoroughly in clear water, and use a stiff-bristle brush to remove any remaining particles. Metal polish can also be used for metallic specimens, if they do not contain metallic acids to damage the specimen. Liquid polish is perhaps more effective than paste, but care must be taken if it contains inflammable ingredients.

A more elaborate method of cleaning native copper, used by the British Museum, is recommended if the specimen is nicely crystallized. Mix one part by weight of stick-form sodium hydroxide (also known as caustic soda or soda lye) with three parts by weight of crystallized Rochelle salt (sodium potassium tartrate). Take care, for this mixture is strongly caustic and will burn moist skin if touched. Dissolve the two chemicals in a glass container, using twenty parts of water, preferably distilled. When not in use, keep the solution in a closed jar to prevent evaporation. Tie a bare copper wire around the specimen to be treated, and suspend it in the solution. Tie the other end of the wire to a stick or ruler, which can be placed across the top of the vessel so that the specimen is left immersed. As the copper compounds dissolve, the solution will turn bluish. Raise and lower the specimen every half hour or so to stir the solution. When it is thoroughly clean, remove the specimen and rinse it thoroughly in running water to remove all the alkali. Soak the specimen for half an hour in a pail of water. If it is not nicely crystallized, the specimen may be scrubbed with scouring powder to bring out the metallic luster. Rinse it in running water and allow it to dry in air.

Native silver also tarnishes easily. The brown, black, or iridescent tarnish is argentite, or silver sulfide. Silver combines with the sulfur present in the air as hydrogen sulfide. Native silver can be cleaned in the same way that silverware is cleaned —by electrolysis. Place the specimen in water in an aluminum pan. Add half an ounce of sodium bicarbonate and half an ounce of common salt to each quart of water. Sal soda or trisodium phosphate can be substituted for the sodium bicarbonate; if so, do not use heat. Otherwise, heat the solution in the pan until the tarnish disappears. If the specimen is not to be lacquered soon, be sure to rinse it thoroughly in hot water, so that it will not tarnish more rapidly than usual. Polish it with a mild abrasive. Silver may also be cleaned with calcium carbonate (precipitated chalk) and a strong ammonia solution. It should then be polished with "rouge" (powdered hematite) on a wet cloth.

Organic incrustations such as algae and lichens frequently mar a specimen. Lichens can be removed by a dilute solution of ammonia, which softens them so that they can be pried or brushed off. Tenacious coatings of algae and lichens can be removed with acid, but if the specimen is a mixed one, this treatment may be too risky. Perhaps sulfuric acid is the most reasonably safe method for cleaning insoluble and noncarbonate minerals. Pry off all large particles of algae or lichens. Smear the concentrated acid on the remaining organic particles, rinse the specimen in water, and scrub it carefully with a brush. The specimen should then be soaked in water for a week or so to remove all traces of the acid.

How to Preserve Your Specimens

Once your minerals are clean, further damage can be prevented in various ways. Most specimens can be lacquered. This coating of a clean, dry surface of the mineral will preserve it from rust, tarnish, and other oxidation. It will also protect it from both absorption of water and loss of moisture, so that it will resist disintegration as well as decomposition. A further advantage is that such specimens can be more readily handled.

To lacquer a specimen that has been cleaned, clean it with a camel's-hair brush to remove all traces of lint particles which may have settled on it from the air. Be sure to protect it from dust while the lacquer dries. Lacquer applied too thickly will crinkle when dry. There are several protective coatings that can be used, some of which are sold commercially as metal lacquers under various names. These consist of nitrocellulose lacquers containing synthetic resins or condensation products.

Other methods of preserving your minerals depend on the individual specimens. Native silver can be prevented from tarnishing by keeping gum camphor in the case with it, or by dipping the specimen in a solution of 95 percent alcohol and 5 percent collodion. The collodion can be removed later with alcohol, should you wish. Lacquer is also appropriate for native silver, native copper, and other metallic specimens.

How to Store Your Specimens

Pyrite and marcasite should be stored in brown paper or boxes. Avoid white paper, because of the chemicals used in its manufacture. Lacquer is a good preservative, but care should be taken first to destroy any labels and trays that have contained "diseased" specimens. Meteorites are best preserved in a gas-tight case filled with dry nitrogen. Where this is not possible, a constant temperature and the use of lacquer have been found helpful. If

the meteorite is to be etched, all cracks should first be filled with shellac to prevent penetration of the acid. Oxidation of nonmetallic minerals, such as vivianite and melanterite, can be prevented by the use of lacquer or an air-tight enclosure.

Some minerals, termed *deliquescent,* become moist upon exposure to damp air and eventually dissolve. Niter, halite, and sylvite are deliquescent, although the latter two are not when they are pure. Such minerals should be kept in a museum jar, either in a dry atmosphere or in a liquid from which the mineral cannot absorb water.

Efflorescent, on the other hand, refers to those minerals that lose water and fall to pieces upon exposure to the atmosphere. Some crystalline hydrates, especially the carbonates and sulfates, may be ruined; epsomite and borax are familiar examples. Such specimens should be lacquered and sealed in glass, or dipped in alcohol and let dry (if copper or iron sulfate minerals), or put in a museum jar filled with water.

How Will Temperature Affect Your Specimens?

Heat and cold have a bad effect on many minerals. An abrupt change of temperature in either direction can destroy susceptible minerals that might not be damaged by ordinary temperature changes. Abnormally high temperatures will cause some minerals to vaporize or melt. Cases should be ventilated, and if light bulbs are used, they should not be left on long. Heat-resistant glass will also prevent damage.

For the average collector, the only temperature problems are those caused by furnace heat and direct sunlight through glass. Many of the efflorescent minerals are sensitive to heat. An example of the effect of heat on a mineral concerns native sulfur. When it is well crystallized, it should not be exposed to direct sunlight. Held in the hand, a specimen will heat sufficiently to crack audibly. Native sulfur and the sensitive sulfides should be kept shaded from direct sunlight. Cold can be equally damaging to some minerals. Quartz, chalcedony, gypsum, calcite, halite, topaz, beryl, and olivine that contain liquid inclusions can be shattered by freezing of the liquid at low temperatures. Such specimens should never be kept in an unheated place.

How Will Light Affect Your Specimens?

Perhaps all minerals are affected in some degree by light, but certain minerals—termed *photosensitive*—are visibly injured by it. Some are decomposed by light; some merely change color without undergoing any chemical or structural change. The silver halides which make photography possible are so sensitive to light as to decompose even in a vacuum. Minerals decomposed by light include bromyrite, cerargyrite, embolite, iodobromite, iodyrite, and miersite. Some of the minerals decomposed by light and oxygen include argentite, chalcocite, cinnabar, cuprite, proustite, pyrargyrite, realgar, and stibnite. Topaz, fluorite, barite, apatite, and rose quartz are among the minerals that are changed only in color by the action of light. A few minerals have a reversible photosensitivity—the change that occurs can be reversed by storing the mineral in the dark or exposing it to light of certain wavelengths of opposite reaction to those that caused the original change. The most notable of such minerals belong to the sodalite group. Photosensitive minerals should be kept in shade, in the dark, or under hinged lids, as even occasional exposure results in eventual damage.

How to Take Care of Your Specimens

It must be emphasized that careless handling is the constant enemy of the mineral collector. Pressure or impact, decomposition or disintegration, temperature changes, or excessive heat or cold all result in mineral damage. Dehydration due to dryness but not preventable by the addition of moisture is another enemy. Opal is especially subject to cracking as it dries. Freshly mined opal has often been "seasoned" by burying it in moist earth. Cut-opal gems can be kept in cotton moistened with olive oil. A common method of preserving opals is to keep them in vials of glycerin.

If certain specimens in your collection become scratched, they can be partly restored by washing them in clear water, scrubbing them with a hard-bristle brush, and coating them lightly with shellac. Fibrous minerals should not be washed; dip them in shellac. Sodium silicate, known as water glass, is also excellent for keeping minerals from scratching.

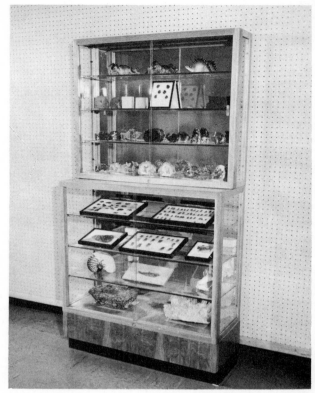

Ward's Natural Science Establishment

The Waddell mineral display cabinet is the newest on the market. Several sizes of units can be put together.

How to Display Minerals

The collector can take real pride in a well-arranged mineral collection. Such a display can be as simple or as elaborate as interest and finances direct. You will very likely begin by using simple storage boxes, but as your collection and your interest grow, you will want to acquire a cabinet or display case to show the specimens to best advantage. Special cases can be purchased, or you can adapt a bookcase, china cabinet, or chest of drawers to suit your individual needs. Portable cases with removable sliding trays are popular with collectors who display their collections at shows or lectures. Trays or drawers that are partitioned to hold the individual specimens are particularly good, for they keep the minerals from touching one another, and they do away with the necessity for handling the specimens overly much.

Large individual specimens can be mounted on blocks of wood or on glass, metal, or plastic stands. The last are attractive, since the plastic can be lettered with a vibrating electric tool. Gems and small crystals show off to advantage in *Riker mounts* —paperbound, glass-covered frames which come in a variety of sizes and can be hung on the wall like pictures. Sand specimens can be kept in individual jars of uniform size and shape, tightly corked and inverted onto pegs or into holes bored into a block of wood. Small, delicate crystals can also be kept in glass vials for better protection. Gems, too, can be displayed in this way, or they may be arranged in trays on dark cloth to bring out their brilliance. If your collection is housed in a cupboard or cabinet, lighting of some kind may be necessary. Concealed strings of white Christmas-tree lights have been used, as have fluorescent tubes. Backing the shelves with mirrors increases the visibility and beauty of a display.

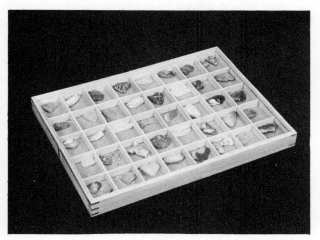

Mineral specimen boxes such as this are most helpful in learning to recognize your own finds.

The possibilities for displaying a collection are limitless, but in every mineral exhibit, the specimens should be neatly trimmed and cleaned and, above all, clearly and carefully labeled. While you will have roughly trimmed most specimens at the spot where you found them, you can greatly improve their appearance by a further trimming at home. Remember, however, that it is accepted practice to leave the matrix in which a crystal is imbedded, for this shows what the original rock associations were and thereby increases the value of the specimen.

Some collectors like to letter the name of a specimen on a piece of adhesive tape or on a patch of white enamel painted on the specimen to identify it. Perhaps most collectors prefer the system that uses only an accession number on the label. This makes a neater looking specimen, but requires a system of cataloging, whereby a list is kept in a card file or notebook, the number of the specimen corresponding to the number and description in the file. For a mineral, the essential information which should go into the file is the number, the name of the species and variety, its composition and associations, and when and where it was found. For a rock, give the number, the name of the specimen, its occurrence, and when and where it was found. As your collection grows, these data will prove invaluable. A small card bearing the basic information concerning a specimen can be placed next to it on display, for quick reference.

What system to use in displaying your collection can sometimes be a problem. Some collectors concentrate on one specific mineral in all its varieties—all the numerous varieties of quartz or of calcite, perhaps. Others prefer to set up their display to emphasize the colors and forms in an attractive way. A popular system which may be used to advantage is arranging your collection according to location, beginning with the minerals and rocks you yourself have collected in your immediate locality, and branching out to cover the county, important regions in the state, and, as you acquire them, specimens from other states and countries. Crystals, meteorites, sands, ores, and gems constitute other specialties.

As your collection and your knowledge grow, you will find that it is impossible to obtain in the field all the interesting specimens you would like to have. Judicious buying, through dealers whose names can be found in the magazines listed in Chapter 12, will add specimens to your collection from all over the world. There are also dealers who maintain stores in many places, where you can select your purchases at first hand. Trading with fellow collectors is just one of the many advantages of belonging to a mineral club. If you trade by mail, make sure that the pertinent information concerning each specimen is enclosed, that

Ward's Natural Science Establishment

Choice pyrite crystals from Leadville, Colorado, have long been popular with mineral collectors.

Ward's Natural Science Establishment

Rich purple fluorite crystals from Rosiclare, Illinois, are among the most attractive minerals for any collection.

A source of strontium, celestite is a commercial mineral of some importance. It is sometimes celestial blue in color.

Foote Mineral Company

Ward's Natural Science Establishment

Pectolite from Paterson, New Jersey, is usually identified by this structure. The mineral has only specimen value.

the mineral is well wrapped, and that the proper postage is affixed. Packages may also be insured as "rough minerals." Rocks and minerals shipped to foreign countries, however, should be marked "rough rocks and minerals—of no commercial value," or the recipient may have to pay duty on the package. Further information should be obtained at your post office.

Growing Crystals at Home

An increasingly popular hobby with many mineral collectors is the growing of crystals artifically. This is a fairly simple procedure which can be done right in your own home. Such artificial crystals, of course, are not real minerals, but watching them grow makes it easier to understand the principles of crystal formation and the conditions existing in nature that control mineral growth. Some interesting and pretty specimens can be grown without a great deal of effort on your part.

There are two general techniques for growing crystals. In the first and simplest method, a saturated solution is put into a mason jar or a covered, flat-bottomed dish. The temperature must remain constant and outside interference kept at a minimum, as variations in the temperature of the solution, the rate of evaporation, and the presence of dust particles or other impurities in the solution will all influence the growth of the crystal. As the solution in the jar or dish slowly evaporates, the upper surface becomes supersaturated with the dissolved salt, which becomes denser and finally sinks to the bottom. Here it adds its excess salt to the growing crystal. A small or "seed" crystal may be used to speed up the growing process. As the liquid loses salt to the crystal, it becomes lighter once more and again rises to the surface. This process continues while the crystal slowly increases in size. Obviously, this method requires little trouble, but constant care.

The second method makes use of a seed crystal suspended by a wire in the solution. This necessitates stirring the solution, as the cycle mentioned above does not operate, and is therefore more trouble, although it may result in larger or better crystals.

Depending upon the sort of crystal you wish to grow, the different salts and their solubilities are listed in any standard chemical handbook. Before a solution can begin to deposit growth on a seed crystal, the maximum amount of salt must be dissolved in it. This solubility increases with temperature. To prepare a stock solution for your crystal growing, it has been suggested that the salt be dissolved in water about 25 percent in excess of the solubility at room temperature. If this solution is then set aside to cool overnight, the excess salt will appear as small crystals—proof that the solution is thoroughly saturated. A thin ring of Vaseline can be smeared on the inside of the dish just above the level of the liquid, to prevent crystalline growth on the sides of the dish.

Temperature changes of any kind are to be avoided, because they will result in cloudy zones in the crystal, dissolving of part of the crystal, or perhaps no growth at all. In a short time, seed crystals will appear in the solution. The two or three largest or best formed should be left to grow, and the excess ones removed. If there are a great many seed crystals, it may be wise to transfer the best to a different dish containing a completely new solution. Slow evaporation will cause these seeds to grow into crystals. If small crystals attach themselves to the larger crystal, they may be removed, and the larger crystal will automatically heal itself. To achieve a more symmetric crystal, turn it over onto a new face each day. Examine the growth daily to assure your control over the enlarging crystal.

A great variety of shapes and colors can be obtained, depending upon what salt you use, whether you add a foreign substance or a drop of dye to the solution, and other factors. Crystals of potassium ferricyanide are a bright, ruby red, while those of potassium ferrocyanide are lemon yellow. Copper sulfate crystals are deep, sky blue; barium chloride and Rochelle salt crystals are colorless. Continual experimentation with different salts and conditions will result in new discoveries for the interested crystal grower, and you may very well notice things that no one has previously recorded.

Join a Rockhound Club

Any mineral collector will find his hobby more enjoyable if he joins a rockhound club. So popular has the hobby of mineral and rock collecting become that clubs are being formed in communities all over the world, and especially in the United States and Canada. These groups meet to discuss and exchange information concerning their hobby, sponsor rock and mineral displays, and go on regularly conducted field trips to obtain new specimens. Many such organizations provide junior memberships for boys and girls to encourage them in this educational, enjoyable, and often profitable hobby. Practically every province in Canada and every state in the Union has one or more groups, and many of the local and state societies are banded together into one of the six regional federations: Eastern, Midwest, Rocky Mountain, Texas, California, and Northwest. These, in turn, are affiliates of the American Federation of Mineralogical Societies. Part of the programs of these federations are the annual conventions, where new discoveries and equipment are highlighted and superb mineral collections are exhibited in competitions. Such a gathering of fellow collectors can make all phases of the mineral hobby more fun, and it is suggested that you get in touch with the nearest club in your vicinity.

Left: The Estwing rock pick is used to pry apart rock slabs and break off excess material. Right: The Estwing rock hammer is another useful form of the mineral collector's and prospector's principal item of equipment.

Trips, Museums, Reading

Whether you belong to a mineral collectors' club or not, you can add to your own knowledge and enjoyment by field trips alone or with others, visits to museums and other places housing mineral displays, and by reading some of the great variety of books and magazines available in mineralogy and related fields.

Perhaps nothing is more enjoyable than a trip into the field, whether with a group, a companion or two, or alone. In the open, the scenery takes on a new meaning when you know that erosion has caused certain rock features, that the presence of certain mineral compounds is responsible for the variety in coloring, and that all of nature has a

story to tell the observant and understanding eye.

Like the camper or hiker, the mineral collector will enjoy his trip more if he wears comfortable

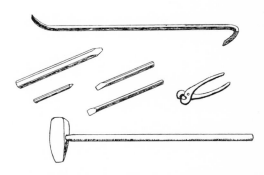

A crowbar, cold chisels, pincers, and a shovel are other useful tools for mineral field work.

and protective clothing. Gloves will guard your hands while you are working with rough rocks. A prospector's hammer, with either a chisel or a pick opposite the hammerhead, is the one indispensable item for the rockhound. Chisels and other tools can be added as needed or desired. A leather or canvas knapsack will serve to carry specimens, which should first be temporarily labeled and wrapped in a thick layer of paper. Cotton or tissue wrapping will cushion delicate minerals, especially crystals. A small notebook is used to write down interesting observations as to location and associations. A pocketknife, a small magnifying glass, and a field guide are useful, too.

Trips to museums can be pleasant as well as informative. You can learn the rocks and minerals native to a given location, along with their usual associations for easier identification. Specimens rare and unknown to the average collector are often housed in museum collections, and methods of display may very well give you ideas for your own collection. For those who are unable to make field trips, the museum or other public mineral display is the best substitute.

Even the shut-in can enjoy the satisfaction of mineral collecting through keeping up with numerous illustrated books and magazines. Current information on rocks and minerals, new finds, and other intriguing information on the subject is thus readily at hand. By trading with other collectors or buying from dealers by mail, the shut-in can build an enviable mineral display.

Chapter 9

GEMOLOGY—THE STUDY
OF PRECIOUS STONES

Chapter 9

GEMOLOGY—THE STUDY OF PRECIOUS STONES

From the time that man first appeared on earth, he has treasured gem stones. In the beginning, he picked up brightly colored pebbles and kept them as he found them, fascinated by their beauty. Later, he strung the rough stones into necklaces and bracelets, and later still, he rounded and polished them. Whether they were first valued for their loveliness alone or for their magic as charms and amulets, it is impossible to determine. Precious stones were certainly credited with mystical and supernatural powers, a belief that lingers even today in the still-popular habit of wearing one's birthstone. Amulets bearing prayers and images from the time of Babylonia and Assyria still exist, and the Egyptian *scarab,* or beetle, symbol of the immortality of the soul, was first fashioned in the 9th Dynasty.

During the classic periods of Greece and Rome, gem engraving became a skilled art. About 300 B.C., the *cameo* was introduced, with its design in relief, in contrast to the older *intaglio,* with its design incised into the surface to serve as a signet. Following the classic age, gem engraving lapsed until the Renaissance and, again, until a revival of interest in the 18th Century.

Gemology may be defined as both the art and the science of precious stones and their man-made substitutes, all of which are attractive enough to be used for personal adornment and decoration. The more common kinds of gem stones are popularly considered semiprecious, but this distinction is far from logical.

Although man-made gems have increased considerably in number and quality in the last few years, most gems are natural minerals. Of the 1,600 or so mineral species, about eighty have been regarded as gems. A few gems, lapis lazuli for example, are rocks. Pearl, coral, amber, and jet are organic gems, the products of living organisms. Artificial, or man-made, gems are creations of the laboratory or factory.

To qualify as a gem, a stone must have beauty, durability, and rarity. The value of a gem varies from place to place and from time to time. It depends on such variables as economic, commercial, and political factors; fashion and demand, supply, cost of cutting and merchandising, and international markets and tariffs all enter the picture. An important consideration in pricing a gem is the perfection of its cutting.

The beauty of a gem depends upon its crystal structure and transparency, brilliance, luster, and color. Some gems, such as turquoise, derive their beauty almost entirely from their color. Because the majority of gem minerals are transparent, however, they depend greatly on luster, refractivity, and clearness for their value.

The coloring of a gem is due chiefly to the presence of chemicals, usually oxides of certain metals, scattered throughout the stone as minute impurities. Diamond, the most universally valuable of all gems, is the only one consisting of a single element —crystallized carbon. Next in simplicity of composition are the oxides, which include corundum (an oxide of aluminum) and quartz (an oxide of silicon). At the opposite end of the scale is tourmaline, with a formula so complex that John Ruskin once wrote: "The chemistry of it is more like a medieval doctor's prescription than the making of a respectable mineral."

The greatest number of gems belong to the silicates, including beryl, jade, garnet, topaz, zircon, and tourmaline. Turquoise and variscite are phosphates; spinel and chrysoberyl are multiple oxides or aluminates. Other gems are sulfides, carbonates, or sulfates. The chief element present in gems is oxygen, with silicon, aluminum, and calcium next in abundance.

The Egyptian scarab is a representation of a beetle. It was the symbol of the soul's immortality.

Gems—Their Crystal Systems

All gem minerals, as well as the man-made synthetics, are crystalline in structure, with the exception of opal. The external shape of a mineral is the outward evidence of its internal atomic structure. Held together by electrical attraction, usually that of oppositely charged ions, the atomic particles are systematically arranged in all directions throughout the crystal, forming a three-dimensional pattern referred to as a *lattice*. The design of this crystal lattice determines the form and other essential properties of the crystal.

There are six main divisions of crystal forms, called *systems*, depending upon the arrangement of axes within the stone. These six systems are further subdivided into thirty-two crystal *classes*, or 230 *space groups*, according to their symmetry. The identification of a gem is largely dependent upon a knowledge of the crystal system to which it belongs: isometric, tetragonal, hexagonal, orthorhombic, monoclinic, or triclinic.

Isometric

Table salt (the mineral halite) is a typical example of an *isometric* crystal, having three axes of equal lengths which meet in the center at right angles. Some isometric gems are spinel, garnet, and diamond. Diamond usually occurs in octahe-

drons resembling two square pyramids base to base, but the sides and angles are the same as in other isometric crystals.

Tetragonal

Crystals of the *tetragonal* system have three axes which meet in the center at right angles, the two horizontal axes being of equal length, the vertical being longer or shorter. Zircon and idocrase are tetragonal gem crystals.

Hexagonal

Some of the finest and largest gem crystals belong to the *hexagonal* system. This six-sided structure, which is also found in snowflakes, possesses four axes, three of which are horizontal and of equal length, and meet in the center at 120-degree angles. The fourth, or vertical axis, at right angles to the others, is always shorter or longer. Quartz is the most familiar hexagonal mineral; corundum (ruby and sapphire), tourmaline, and beryl (emerald and aquamarine) are other important hexagonal gems.

Orthorhombic

Orthorhombic crystals are often complex in form, having three axes which meet in the center at right angles, each of a different length. Topaz, olivine, and chrysoberyl are well-known members of the orthorhombic system.

Monoclinic

Spodumene (kunzite), orthoclase feldspar (moonstone), and sphene belong to the *monoclinic* system, which is characterized by three axes, each of a different length. Two of the axes meet at right angles, and the third is inclined forward and downward.

Triclinic

The sixth crystal system, the *triclinic*, has three axes which meet in the center at oblique angles and are of different lengths. Both microcline feldspar (amazonstone) and plagioclase feldspar (labradorite) belong to the triclinic system.

Gems—Their Luster

Luster, which refers to the appearance of the surface of a gem in reflected light, is another very important property of a gem stone. The greater the reflection, the brighter a gem will appear. Hard stones, which can usually be given a higher degree of polish, allow less light to penetrate, and so more will be reflected. A soft gem or one with a granular texture scatters the light, resulting in a diffused luster. Many descriptive terms are applied to various kinds of luster. *Adamantine* is typical of diamond; *vitreous* (or glassy) luster is typical of most gems; zircon and andradite garnet are gems possessing *subadamantine* luster, which exceeds that of glass but is not equal to that of diamond. Amber is the only familiar gem which has a *resinous* luster. *Greasy* luster refers to gems having an oily surface; turquoise has a *waxy* luster, pearl is *pearly,* and fibrous gems, such as satin spar, show a *silky* luster. Pyrite and hematite, opaque, metallic gems, have a *metallic* luster.

Gems—Their Optics

Refraction is the term used to describe the light that is neither reflected nor absorbed at the surface of a gem, but enters the interior. As it does so, the ray of light is slowed, causing it to be bent. This deflection can be determined mathematically and expressed by a number known as the *refractive index.* Gems with a high refractive index are termed *optically dense.* As the light comes out of a gem, it is refracted in a different direction. Light that reaches the so-called critical angle inside a stone can no longer be refracted out of the gem and is totally reflected so that it stays inside. Total internal reflection occurring at the bottom of a gem causes the light to be returned to the top and refracted out from there, adding to the stone's brilliancy.

A *refractometer* is an instrument designed to measure the refractive index of a gem. While the range of standard refractometers is not high enough to measure diamond, zircon, sphene, and andradite garnet, other gems can be measured by placing one of the facets of a cut stone against the refractometer lens, using a drop of highly refractive oil to bring lens and facet into optical contact. Light is then directed through the lens and against the flat bottom surface of the stone. The portion of the light that strikes at more than the critical angle is totally reflected, producing a band of light,

the edge of which is read on a graduated scale.

Fire in a gem refers to the spread of colors when white light is separated into its component colors. In this *dispersion,* each color of the spectrum is refracted to a different extent; red light rays are bent the least, violet the most. In colored stones, these hues are usually disguised by the color of the stone itself.

Double refraction is found in gems belonging to the five crystal systems other than isometric. These gems split the single ray into two rays, each ray having a different refractive index. This double refraction can be seen with the aid of a magnifying glass in olivine and zircon, although a microscope or jeweler's lens may be needed to detect it in other gems. A doubly refractive gem will show two parallel lines on the refractometer. The difference between these two readings is called *birefringence.*

The Rayner refractometer measures the light-bending power of a gem. The value obtained serves to identify the gem.

By use of the *spectroscope,* we can measure and analyze light that has undergone dispersion. In a direct-vision spectroscope, a full normal spectrum is seen when it is pointed at a light source. When a gem is held between the spectroscope and the light, vertical dark lines appear, obscuring sections of the spectrum. These are called *absorption bands* and represent the rays that have been removed by the chemical impurities in the gem. Each element results in a characteristic arrangement of the absorption bands, making up an *absorption spectrum.* Thus, two gems of the same color may prove to absorb light differently because they are composed of chemical combinations that are completely unlike. Zircon, emerald, and almandite garnet are readily identified in this way.

Gems having double refraction also possess a twin-color effect known as *dichroism,* due to the fact that each of the two rays is not only refracted dif-

American Museum of Natural History

The Zuñi Indians are among the best artisans in creating jewelry set with turquoise. This is a Holy Toad.

Ward's Natural Science Establishment

Green feldspar, known as amazonstone, is abundant in Colorado. These crystals came from Crystal Peak, near Florissant, in the Pikes Peak region.

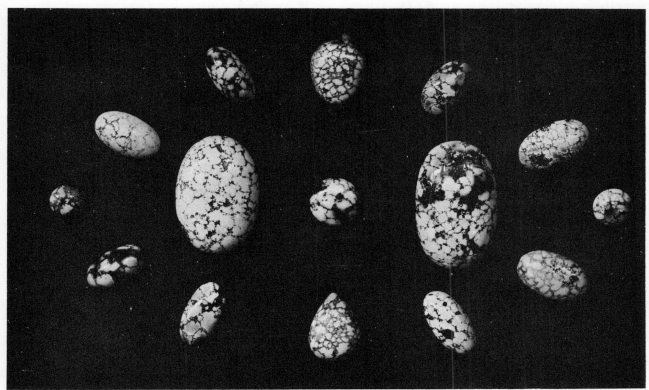

Any gem having a rounded top is called a cabochon. These are fashioned from turquoise mined in Mohave County, Arizona.

This sardonyx cameo is carved from a reddish variety of chalcedony quartz. The stone is related to carnelian.

ferently from the other, but is absorbed to a different extent and has a different color. To see this twin-color effect, a *dichroscope* is used. A common model is a short tube with a round opening at one end and a square opening at the other. Inside is fastened a piece of clear calcite (Iceland spar); a magnifying lens may also be added. The gem to be examined is held just beyond the square opening. By looking through the round opening, the viewer can see two squares of color side by side, which will change places slowly as the dichroscope is rotated. Not all doubly refractive gems show dichroism, and of course no colorless gem can be dichroic. Also, the viewer must look at the gem in more than two directions, since there is no double refraction along certain optical axes in crystals. Ruby, blue sapphire, and emerald are among the gems most easily identified by using the dichroscope.

Ward's Natural Science Establishment

The Rayner dichroscope has the ability to separate colored light into its component hues. It is an effective instrument for identifying gems.

Gems—Their Weight

Gems are usually weighed in *carats* (not to be confused with *karat,* referring to the purity of gold alloy). A carat was originally the weight of a seed of the carob, or locust, tree of the Mediterranean. Today's carat equals one-fifth of a gram; about 150 carats equal an ounce. Each carat consists of 100 *points.* Pearls are sold by the *pearl grain,* four grains equaling one carat.

Gems having the same size differ greatly in weight due to their *density,* or (properly) their *specific gravity.* Zircon, for example, is heavier than diamond, chiefly because the elements of which it

is composed—zirconium, oxygen, and silicon—have greater atomic weights than the single element, carbon, of diamond. Amber is the lightest gem; cassiterite is the heaviest.

Gems—Their Durability

To wear well and retain its beauty over the years, a gem must be fairly hard. The capacity of a gem to withstand the effects of abrasion, impact, and chemical action is called *durability*. The durability of a gem depends on its *hardness,* or resistance to scratching, and its *toughness*, or resistance to breakage. These properties may depend upon the crystal direction. Under pressure or a blow, a stone will split in regular directions along its "grain." This splitting is referred to as *cleavage.* Only a crystalline gem has cleavage; amorphous gems can break only with a *fracture,* which has no regular direction. Crystalline gems may have both cleavage and fracture, but the cleavage usually predominates.

How Gems Occur

Gems occur in a variety of ways. Perhaps they are most commonly found in igneous-rock formations. The diamond-bearing rock of South African volcanoes is called kimberlite and is a basic igneous rock. Pegmatite, which is known for its coarse texture and large crystals, is the source of a great many gem minerals, including topaz, tourmaline, and rose quartz. Metamorphic rocks produce garnet, jade, and lapis lazuli, as well as other gem minerals and rocks. The most important secondary sources of gems are placers, or gravel deposits. Diamond, chrysoberyl, ruby, and sapphire are especially significant in such sedimentary beds. Formed originally in primary or in metamorphic rocks, then released by weathering and transported by stream action, these gems are often found in rich concentration in placers. Africa's alluvial diamond beds, Ceylon's gem gravels, and Montana's sapphire fields along the Missouri River are typical placers. Special sources of gems include hot springs and the interiors of geodes. The organic gems amber and jet are found in ancient sedimentary deposits. The associations of certain gems with certain minerals and rocks are quite typical, and a knowledge of these relationships often aids in the discovery of gems. Some of the gems associated with African diamonds, for example, are zircon, olivine, and pyrope garnet. In Brazil, diamond is associated with corundum, zircon, garnet, tourmaline, and quartz.

Where Gems Are Found

Ceylon, India, Africa, and South America (especially Brazil) are the great world sources of precious stones. The United States has produced a large variety of gem stones, but it has few deposits of major importance. The most important factor in United States gem-stone production is considered to be the thousands of amateur collectors around the country who search for and collect gems as a hobby. At least one kind of gem stone occurs in every state—agate being the most widespread. Topaz is found in New England and most of the Western states; jade is found in Alaska, Wyoming, and California. Turquoise is available in many Western states, from both turquoise mines and copper mines. Montana is known for sapphire, and North Carolina is a source of ruby. Maine and California have yielded tourmaline, as have other states in minor quantities. While diamonds in small numbers have been found from North Carolina to California and from Georgia to Wisconsin, with the Great Lakes region being the most widespread diamond "field" in the United States, the only place where diamonds have been mined commercially is in Pike County, Arkansas. The rest are of scattered occurrence, and their original source is still unknown.

Gem Cutting and Polishing

Hobbyists and commercial gem cutters alike make use of the same lapidary techniques. *Faceting,* which is characterized by smooth, flat surfaces —facets—is used chiefly on transparent gems to bring out their brilliance and fire. *Cabochon cutting* —the rounding and polishing of a stone—is used to show the beauty of opaque or translucent gems having an appealing color, pattern, or unusual effect. In the gem-cutting industry, a distinction is made between diamond cutters and other gem cutters (or lapidaries), since diamond cutting requires such highly trained skill. There are five distinct activities in this craft. An inspector or marker first examines the rough diamonds for crystal form and marks off with india ink those parts of the crystal to be kept or removed. Following notching, a cleaver splits the diamond along the lines of growth. The stone is then handed over to the cutter, who removes the imperfections and gives the stone its shape. The polisher then cuts or grinds the facets.

Cabochon cutting is the simplest of lapidary work and is the technique most commonly employed by amateur gem cutters, though many of them also do faceting. If larger specimens are used, the gem area must be sawed from the rough mass. Smaller fragments go directly to the grinding wheel, which removes blemishes and other undesired parts. Then, sanding takes away the scratches caused by grinding. The final step is, of course, the polishing. Gem cutting has become a popular hobby in the United States—even high schools and colleges teach courses in lapidary work.

Tumbling is the process of rounding gems mechanically for setting in informal jewelry. A metal or wood drum is kept in constant rotation, except when the abrasive is changed to a finer grit.

Ward's Natural Science Establishment

The Hillquist tumbler is typical of the equipment used to make tumbled gems by rotating them with an abrasive. A single batch may go for days or weeks.

Gems for the Collector

Many of the gem stones that the collector and prospector are likely to come across are described on the following pages.

Diamond

Diamond has long been regarded as the king of gems. It is the hardest of all substances, and its brilliance and beauty make it prized throughout the world. The first diamonds came from India, and most of the famous stones of history are Indian diamonds. Later, around 1720, as India's supply diminished, diamonds were found in Brazil. Then, in 1867, Schalk van Niekirk offered to buy an unusual stone which he saw in a farmhouse in South Africa. It was only a toy for the children, he was told, and the stone was given to him. A mineralogist identified it as a diamond worth several thousand dollars, and thus began the great diamond history of South Africa. Diamonds there are found chiefly in *pipes* (the necks of ancient volcanoes) in a rock called kimberlite. Secondary sources are alluvial, or placer, deposits —the result of erosion and later accumulation. Some diamonds have had a famous history—the Orloff, the Koh-i-noor, and the huge Cullinan, which weighed 3,025 carats and was the size of a man's fist. Colored diamonds are rare; noted ones include the Hope (blue), the Dresden (green), and the Tiffany (orange).

Many plants and factories depend to a great extent on industrial diamonds: to true up grinding wheels, to turn machine tools, as dies, as core drills, and in numerous other uses. Diamond can even be used to measure the intensity of atomic radiation.

Corundum—Ruby and Sapphire

Ruby and sapphire both belong to the species *corundum.* Corundum ranks next in hardness to diamond; in addition, ruby and sapphire have no cleavage, making them the most durable of ring stones. Although sapphire is popularly thought of

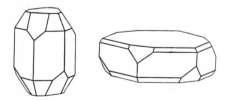

Corundum includes both ruby and sapphire. Crystals like these come from Burma.

as being only blue in color, the name refers to all corundum gems except the red ruby. Sapphires can be green or pink or purple—even golden. Exceedingly popular in recent years has been the star sapphire, which, when properly cut, exhibits a six-rayed star across its surface. The principal source of corundum in all its varieties is the Orient, although some sapphires come from Australia and Montana.

Chrysoberyl

Alexandrite and cat's-eye both belong to the species *chrysoberyl,* although they are as different from each other as could be. Alexandrite, found originally in Russia and more recently in Ceylon, is a rare gem which has been called "an emerald by day, an amethyst by night"; it is green in daylight, but turns raspberry red under artificial light. True cat's-eye (not to be confused with the variety of quartz sometimes called the same thing) possesses a gleaming band of light which moves across it as light does in the eye of a cat—hence its name. The most popular colors of this charming stone are honey yellow, apple green, and dark green.

Sphalerite

Sphalerite is an example of a gem too soft and too easily breakable, as well as too rare, to achieve great popularity. Yet, its dispersion is much greater than that of diamond, and its luster and brilliance make it a radiant stone. This gem is yellowish brown in color and is found almost exclusively in Mexico and Spain. The mineral sphalerite in its ordinary brown-to-black form is quite common, for it is the chief ore of zinc.

Cassiterite

Cassiterite, sometimes called tinstone because it is the ore of tin, is rarely seen as jewelry. When it is transparent enough, however, cassiterite makes a very lovely gem stone. It has a diamondlike luster and a deep, golden color. It is the heaviest of all the gems.

Fluorite

Vases and other ornamental carvings were once cut from opaque English *fluorite,* known as bluejohn. Later, gems were cut from the transparent variety. Green, yellow, pink, purple, and colorless fluorite have been found, but its cleavage and low degree of hardness makes this mineral difficult to cut.

Brazilianite

Brazilianite, named for the country in which it was discovered, was added to the ranks of known minerals (and gems) as recently as 1945. Transparent and of a chartreuse yellow, it is a novel and pretty stone, though it lacks adequate hardness and brilliance.

Apatite

A fairly common mineral, *apatite* is found only rarely in gem quality. It has a great many colors; the yellowish green variety is called asparagus-stone. It stands number 5 in Mohs' scale of hardness, which means that it does not have sufficient durability for use in jewelry.

Pyroxene

The *pyroxene* group of minerals includes such gems as enstatite, a transparent, green stone; diopside, which is more of a bottle-green in color; and spodumene, a fragile, dainty gem found in yellow, green, and lilac hues. The green spodumene is called hiddenite, and the lilac variety is known as kunzite.

Benitoite

Benitoite was first mistaken for sapphire, but it was seen through a dichroscope to have twin colors of blue and white. It is a rare gem, and it comes only in small sizes. The home of benitoite is California.

Tourmaline

One of the wonders of the gem world is *tourmaline,* and it is increasing in popularity among collectors every year. Unsurpassed for its diversity of color, it varies from completely colorless and transparent to opaque and black—including practically every known shade and tint. Many specimens show several colors, and some rare crystals have blue and green at opposite ends. "Watermelon tourmaline" has a red center, a green outer border, and a zone of white between. Because of this great range and combination of colors, tourmaline has been called "the rainbow gem."

Its crystal structure, as well as its chemical composition, is complex. The crystals occur in prisms having a rounded, triangular outline, with lines and furrows along their length. If an individual crystal is heated or cooled, it becomes electrically charged—positive at one end, negative at the other. Ceylon, Russia, Madagascar, and Africa have yielded fine tourmaline, as have California (in San Diego and Riverside Counties) and Maine.

Maine has long been a noteworthy source of fine crystals of tourmaline. The mineral comes in a variety of pretty colors.

Beryl

Several gems belong to the mineral species called *beryl.* The name beryl itself is reserved for the pale-green gem variety of this mineral, while its other varieties are termed emerald, aquamarine, morganite, heliodor, and goshenite. Colorless, massive beryl resembles common milky quartz, but crystallized, colorless beryl (sometimes called goshenite) is as transparent as glass. Among the most valued of precious stones are emerald and aquamarine.

Lacking in brilliance and fire, and even to some extent in durability, emerald is still treasured as one of the rarest of gems because of its transparent, velvety-green color. Since the times of Alexander the Great and Cleopatra, emerald has been greatly prized. The conquistadors stole vast quantities of emeralds from the Incas of Colombia—which today still produces the finest emeralds in the world. The parallel, steplike pattern of cutting used for emerald is so characteristic that it has been named the *emerald cut.* (Some diamonds are emerald cut, while in turn some emeralds are cut in the *brilliant* style commonly used for diamond.)

The name aquamarine is Latin for "sea water," and the stone is a beautiful blend of blue and green, varying in color like the ocean. Romans, Renaissance artists, and the natives of India are among those who have valued aquamarine as a gem stone. Brazil is the chief source of today's aquamarines; others are found in Madagascar, Siberia, and Ceylon, and a few in the United States. The highest mineral locality in North America is an aquamarine deposit atop Mount Antero in Colorado, more than 14,000 feet above sea level.

The star on the sapphire is due to the presence of tiny fibers or other inclusions. A curved top is necessary to bring the rays to a focus. These are (l. to r.) the Edith Haggin de Long Star Ruby, the Star of India, and the Midnight Star Sapphire.

Nevada is a leading producer of turquoise. This material came from Esmeralda County, Nevada.

This tourmaline crystal from Mount Mica, Paris, Maine, is of exceptional quality. The locality is an historic one.

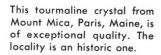

This parcel of diamonds weighs 15,000 carats. It has been recovered from the Dutoitspan mine, Union of South Africa.

N. W. Ayer & Son

Topaz crystals from Brazil may weigh hundreds of pounds, yet be perfectly clear. Topaz is a hard and heavy gem stone.

H. C. Dake

Morganite is a beryl gem ranging in color from pink and rose to a rich, rose red. Yellow beryl is called heliodor, meaning "gift of the sun," and contains a radioactive substance that intensifies its brightness and color.

Peridot

The gem variety of the mineral olivine is called *peridot*. A good specimen has a rich, bottle-green color unlike that of any other gem, although the Crusaders brought many of these stones back to Europe in the belief that they were emeralds.

Garnet

Garnet is a group of minerals having half a dozen subspecies, five of which have gem varieties of their own. While garnet is commonly thought of as being reddish brown, it occurs in nearly every color except blue. Garnet is rather highly refractive and, because it lacks cleavage, is not easily broken. There are two general series—the almandite series (which includes pyrope, almandite, and spessartite), and the andradite series (which includes grossularite, andradite, and uvarovite). Uvarovite yields no gems, only because its crystals are too small.

Pyrope is the most commonly known gem garnet. It has a fiery coloring, red with a yellowish cast, and is called Bohemian garnet from its original chief place of origin. It is frequently sold as a variety of ruby. Rhodolite, a lovely rose-colored variety, is found only in tiny crystals. Almandite, known for 2,000 years as carbuncle, and termed precious garnet in India, has a deep, clear, red color, usually tinged with violet. It was a favorite of Roman gem engravers, and fine specimens of intaglios and cameos are found in gem collections in Europe. Too uncommon and too small to be well known is spessartite, which is red with a golden or brownish cast.

Garnets of the andradite series include the gems grossularite and andradite. Grossularite is named from the Latin word for gooseberry, because the hazy, spotted stones of granular structure are the color of gooseberries. Golden-brown varieties are called hessonite (or cinnamon-stone); orange stones are known as hyacinth-garnet, and reddish-brown gems are termed jacinth-garnet. The colors of andradite are yellow, black, and green. To-pazolite is so called from its resemblance to yellow topaz. Most remarkable of all the garnets, however, is demantoid, the diamondlike green garnet. It has the most extreme display of rainbow colors of any major precious stone. In the choicest variety, it is a pure emerald green, with fine brilliance and luster. Because it is rare, small in size, and not particularly durable, it is most frequently set to enhance other gems, such as diamond.

Zircon

One of the oldest gems, but until recently a mineralogical mystery, *zircon* is an extraordinary gem. Its great range of colors, its luster and brilliance, and its high specific gravity are all characteristics adding to its value and beauty. In fact, a well-cut, colorless zircon resembles a diamond so closely that many people cannot distinguish between them. At the turn of the century, zircon was divided into high, low, and intermediate types, according to physical and optical properties. It has now been shown that the "high zircon" is the normal kind, which, when broken down gradually by the presence of radioactive thorium, finally becomes "low zircon." As the structure varies, so does the coloring: deep red, green, golden yellow, blue, and colorless. Following World War I, an industry was established to alter zircon by heat in order to produce certain artificial colors of much loveliness. Reddish-brown stones become golden yellow or colorless when heated in air, blue or colorless when heated in a vacuum. The finest zircons are a product of the Orient, where most of the heat treating and cutting of the stones is done.

Topaz

The velvety luster, perfect transparency, and many colors of *topaz* make this gem stone one of the most popular. Yet, the cost of topaz remains relatively low, due to its rather common occurrence. Topaz crystals have unusually smooth faces and sharp edges. While it ranks fourth among gems in hardness, topaz possesses an extremely easy cleavage parallel to the base. It is frequently associated with tin ore. Although the rich, golden-yellow tints of topaz are the most familiar and popular, there are numerous other shades. Incidentally, not all yellow stones are topaz, as is popularly believed; citrine, a yellow quartz, is often confused with true topaz. Colorless topaz and blue, green, and brownish hues are frequent. The application of heat to brownish topaz results in lovely colorings of rose and pink and sherry red. Brazil, Ceylon, and Russia produce much topaz; good sources are also Japan, Australia, the British Isles, and parts of Africa. New England and the Western states have provided outstanding crystals; massive topaz is mined industrially in South Carolina.

Axinite

A rare gem of unusual coloring is *axinite,* with its wedge-shaped crystals and shades of violet blue, olive brown, and honey yellow. The only transparent gem besides kyanite in the triclinic crystal system, axinite is about as hard as quartz and has a strong dichroism.

Andalusite

Andalusite is another gem mineral of strongly dichroic nature. Usually brown or green, it often resembles tourmaline when faceted. A less valuable variety, chiastolite, is not faceted, but it is

Cornelius S. Hurlbut, Jr.

Cross-shaped inclusions of carbon occur in chiastolite. It is a variety of andalusite.

polished in sections to show the black cross formation in the center of the crystal, which is due to the arrangement of carbon within the stone.

Kyanite

Kyanite is the only mineral to have a variable hardness; it can resist the scratch of a knife in any direction except down the length of the crystal. It has the choice color of blue sapphire; the long blades of its triclinic crystals usually concentrate the color in the center, leaving an outer margin of white.

Sphene

Gem *sphene* has a number of amazing optical properties to make it a notable addition to any

gem collection. Its refractive index is so high that a standard refractometer shows no reading. Its dispersion or fire is greater than is shown by all the major gems, including diamond, with the exception of andradite garnet. Sphene also possesses a surface luster of sparkling brilliance and the greatest dichroism of all the gems. Its wedge-shaped crystals are found in green and yellow, light and dark brown. However, they are deficient in hardness.

Malachite

While its softness prevents *malachite* from being set in rings, this silky, banded, green gem is much used in necklaces, pins, and even buttons. In Czarist Russia, it was a favorite stone when carved into vases, jewel boxes, bowls, and table tops. Gem malachite has an agatelike banding, and material of outstanding quality comes from the Congo.

Turquoise

Turquoise has been highly regarded as a gem stone over the centuries, in Egypt, Persia, Tibet, and the Middle East, and, of course, by the American Indian. Blue, green, or a blend of both, turquoise has a waxy luster which helps to conceal scratches; this mineral is not, however, very hard. It occurs in irregular lumps, crusts, or veins in broken rock that is often volcanic in origin. Small patches and streaks of kaolin and limonite result in attractive patterns, and these are generally accepted as proof of genuineness. Iranian turquoise is considered the best.

Variscite

A mineral easily confused with turquoise is *variscite,* which is usually light green or bluish green. In recent years, it has increased in use and popularity, though it is found extensively only in northern Utah.

The Feldspar Gems

While the abundant group of minerals known as *feldspar* is chiefly important to the geologist and maker of ceramics, several gem varieties in this group are worth mentioning. Because of similar structural peculiarities, most of them occur in more than one kind of feldspar. Moonstone is an orthoclase feldspar, attractive in pins, necklaces, and beads. It has a deceptively milky appearance until the stone is turned, when it then glows with a soft radiance.

Green microcline feldspar is amazonstone. With its tints of bluish green, bright green, and greenish gray, it is often mistaken for jade. The outstanding American locality for amazonstone is the Pikes Peak region of Colorado. Three of the six species of plagioclase feldspar are of gem quality: albite, oligoclase, and labradorite. Albite, as the name suggests, is white, and it sometimes occurs as moonstone. Closely related to albite is oligoclase, which also furnishes some moonstone. Most striking is a golden-red and yellow variety of oligoclase aptly named sunstone, or aventurine feldspar. The latter name comes from its resemblance to the artificial glass known today as goldstone, but the gleaming effect in the feldspar is due to minute flecks of hematite distributed throughout. A most beautiful feldspar is labradorite, with its lovely iridescent play of colors. Repeated crystal twinning in this otherwise common mineral (first found along the coast of Labrador) turns it into a sheet of peacock brightness—blue and green or golden red or yellow.

Lapis Lazuli

Four opaque blue minerals make up *lapis lazuli*. One of them, sodalite, sometimes occurs by itself as a distinct gem. It has a deeper, more violet blue than the rest, and it has been found in gem quality in Canada, in Maine, and at Mount Vesuvius.

Lapis lazuli has been prized by many nations and races since Biblical times, when it was called sapphire. Babylonian and Assyrian jewelry included primitive seals of lapis lazuli. Chinese lapidaries carved it into such objects as snuff bottles. Beads and sets for pins are the most common European and American uses for the stone. It is a rich-blue stone, spangled with gold and white; Pliny compared it to the night sky bedecked with stars. Pyrite is responsible for the golden flecks; calcite furnishes the white veining. In 1271, Marco Polo saw the ancient lapis lazuli mines of Afghanistan. Today, good material also comes from Siberia and Chile.

Prehnite

The first mineral to be named in honor of a person, *prehnite* (named for Colonel Von Prehn in 1783) is occasionally used as a gem. It is translucent, light green, and sometimes looks like pale jade.

True Jade: Jadeite and Nephrite

True jade is either *jadeite* or *nephrite,* two distinct minerals which resemble each other so completely that only experts can tell the difference. From ancient times, jade was used for implements and weapons. The Chinese have always regarded it as the noblest of gems, working it into some of the most beautiful carvings in the world. Other jade figures and carvings belong to the art of prehistoric Switzerland, early Central America, and New Zealand. The chief characteristic of jade is its great toughness—it is virtually immune to breakage. This is due to the characteristic compact aggregate of crystals, which are so intimately intergrown that they are difficult to separate. Chemically pure jade is white, but the gem is much more likely to vary in color from blue, yellow, and mottled shades to the more familiar green.

Jadeite is the more expensive of the two kinds of jade, because it is the more rare. It includes the famous imperial jade, mutton-fat jade, and such varieties as mauve, blood red, and vivid yellow. Dark-green or almost black jadeite is termed chloromelanite. Metamorphic in origin, jadeite is found in dikes in a green serpentine rock, or, if eroded by streams or glaciers, it will be found in scattered boulders.

Nephrite, belonging to the amphibole group of minerals, is more common than jadeite and has a lesser range of colors. It is usually more opaque, and when polished, it has an oily rather than a vitreous luster. Even tougher than jadeite, it has a fibrous structure. Alaska yields a good deal of nephrite, and during some recent years, nephrite has led American gem production by virtue of the jade prospecting in Wyoming, particularly around Lander.

Rhodonite

An opaque, pink mineral which occurs both massive and in translucent crystals, *rhodonite* of gem quality is found in New South Wales, New Jersey, Sweden, and Russia. Russian gem cutters have created lavish carvings in rhodonite. A favorite gift at the Czarist court was a rhodonite Easter egg.

Chrysocolla

Greenish-blue *chrysocolla,* with either a vitreous or an enamellike luster, is used in bracelets and pendants. This gem has a worldwide occurrence, being associated with other copper minerals.

Idocrase

Once called vesuvianite because it was first identified from Mount Vesuvius, *idocrase* is found either in transparent crystals of green, brown, and yellow, or in compact masses resembling jade. The latter variety is called californite.

Staurolite

Staurolite, known as fairy stone or cross stone, is the only gem other than pearl to be worn in its natural state. A hole is drilled so that the cross-shaped crystals can be worn around the neck on a chain. Two orthorhombic twin crystals penetrate each other nearly at right angles to form the cross. A metamorphic mineral, staurolite is found in Switzerland, Germany, France, Scotland, and Brazil. It is also abundant in certain places in the United States, chiefly in Georgia, Virginia, North Carolina, and New Mexico.

The quartz minerals and rocks are so numerous and varied and they produce so many fine gem materials that they are discussed separately in Chapter 10.

Chapter 10

THE QUARTZ
MINERALS AND ROCKS

Chapter 10

THE QUARTZ MINERALS AND ROCKS

Quartz, with its more than 200 varieties and subvarieties, is unquestionably the mineral most familiar to the prospector and the collector. It is characteristic of igneous, sedimentary, and metamorphic rocks; it is found in rocks of all geologic ages and environments. Because it is so durable a mineral, quartz is often found on the surface, after even the hard rock matrix in which it occurred has long since weathered away. Hence, quartz *float* guides the prospector to many an ore-bearing vein, and suggests to the collector the presence of granite pegmatite, which may yield fine large crystals of other minerals as well as quartz. Cavities in several kinds of rock are frequently lined or filled with quartz. It is an important constituent of many rocks, such as granite and gneiss; it occurs as a rock itself in the forms of conglomerate, sandstone, and quartzite; and the sands of the seashore consist mainly of quartz.

Because of its beauty, durability, and unlimited variety of colors, patterns, and textures, quartz has been the favorite gem stone of the amateur lapidary ever since primitive man crudely polished the first agate. Some of the loveliest gems are quartz, as are some of the most handsome mineral specimens, too.

Quartz, tridymite, and cristobalite are each composed of silica (silicon dioxide), but they originate at different temperatures and have different atomic structures. Opal consists of silica and a varying amount of water. These minerals may all be thought of as belonging to the same group.

Quartz has a hardness of 7, marking the division between the hard and soft minerals. It cannot be scratched by a knife, but it will easily scratch glass. Its crystalline varieties (*quartz* proper) are vitreous (or glassy) in appearance, ranging from translucent to transparent. Cryptocrystalline (or finely textured) varieties—known as *chalcedony*—are extremely fine grained, and have a compact, flinty appearance and a waxy luster. Some authorities consider chalcedony an independent mineral, while others regard it as a mixture of quartz and opal (hydrous silica gel). Lapidaries treat the two types as separate gem minerals, since quartz is usually faceted, while chalcedony is best cut into cabochons.

Crystalline Varieties of Quartz

Quartz crystals are hexagonal, and a perfect crystal forms a prism, coming to a point at both ends. Such crystals are uncommon, because double-ended crystals can form only when growth in all directions is freely possible. A typical crystal is attached at one end, and only the other end is able to grow to a point. Some crystals are so small as to be visible only under a magnifying glass—a surface covered with such crystals is termed *drusy* —but single crystals have been discovered that weigh a number of tons. Many crystals are so poorly formed that the hexagonal shape is not immediately recognizable. *Striations*—horizontal lines on the vertical faces—help the mineral collector feel more sure of identifying quartz. There is also a great deal of massive quartz to be found, in which crystal faces are not evident at all.

Amethyst

The most precious of all the quartz gems is *amethyst;* its beautiful colors range from pale orchid to deep purple. It has been used for ornamental purposes since Biblical times. The name comes from a Greek word meaning "not drunken," for the ancients believed that the stone would prevent or cure intoxication. According to Pliny, this superstition arose from the color of amethyst, which is almost but not quite the color of wine. Amethyst ornaments and seals are found in the tombs of the Babylonians and Egyptians; amethyst beads have been found in old Anglo-Saxon graves in Great Britain. Perhaps the oldest of England's royal jewels is the large amethyst in the crown of Edward the Confessor, who was made king in 1042. For centuries, until the discovery of large deposits in South America, amethyst was expensive. Today it is no less pretty, but much more reasonable in cost. Structurally, amethyst consists of an intricate arrangement of twinned particles containing layers and patches of color, which seem to be due to iron impurities. Cavities or veins in granite and other igneous rocks are good sources of amethyst, which usually occurs in a drusy growth. In South America—notably Brazil and Uruguay—it occurs in agate geodes, lining the walls of these hollow concretions. Amethyst is found around the world, good specimens coming from Ceylon, Japan, Siberia, South Africa, and India. In the United States, gem-quality amethyst has been collected in Montana, Michigan, Virginia, North Carolina, and Arizona.

Aventurine

Quartz containing tiny flakes of mica or hematite, which give it a spangled appearance, is called *aventurine*. It can be brown or red or green, with the flakes adding a sparkle to the specimen and making it popular as a gem stone. An imitation material, made of glass and copper filings and called goldstone, is used in novelty jewelry. Strangely enough, the mineral derives its name from the imitation, rather than the other way around. Goldstone, or aventurine, was first made accidentally in Venice by a glassmaker; only later was the natural material discovered.

Citrine

Citrine is yellow quartz; its name is derived from the Latin word for lemon. Citrine owes its color to ferric iron oxide, and ranges in color from a pale, yellowish green through lemon yellow to reddish orange. Specimens having a somewhat brownish tint are the most common. Because it looks so much like topaz that even some jewelers do not realize the difference, citrine has been termed "false topaz." (True topaz is a much more rare and far more expensive gem mineral.) Most of the world's supply of citrine comes from Brazil, though specimens are found in Madagascar and a few other lands.

Quartz crystals are numerous in New York State. The most familiar ones are spoken of as Herkimer diamonds. They are often clear and lustrous.

Rock Crystal

Clear, colorless, lustrous quartz is called *rock crystal*. All crystals derive their name from the original discovery by the Greeks of rock crystal in the Alps, for they first thought it to be a kind of ice (or *krystallos*), which had become permanently frozen. Later, all regularly shaped minerals were termed crystals. Rock crystal is common throughout the world: in the European Alps, in Madagascar and Japan, and particularly in Brazil. In North America, it is abundant near Hot Springs, Arkansas, and tiny crystals, called "Herkimer diamonds," are found in Herkimer County, New York. The mineral is popular as a gem, and it has been used for centuries in crystal-gazing. The largest perfect crystal ball in the world, weighing 107 pounds, is on display in the United States National Museum. Perfect rock crystal is used in optical apparatus, and it came into extensive use in radio and radar instruments during World War II. Most optical-quality rock crystal is imported from Brazil.

When cracks appear in rock crystal, making it

iridescent, it is called rainbow quartz or iris quartz. The natural rainbow quartz can be imitated by heating rock crystal and cooling it quickly, and this is frequently done.

Milky Quartz

Milky quartz is so called because the presence of numerous liquid inclusions reduces the transparency of rock crystal, giving it a milky appearance. This is a common type of quartz, found in veins and in pegmatites, and is an important source of gold and other precious metals. It is a massive quartz, prevalent in most of the igneous and metamorphic rocks. During the numerous gold rushes of the 19th Century, a popular souvenir of the mining camps was milky quartz containing particles of gold. This was cut into jewelry and called gold quartz.

Sagenite

Sagenite is a form of rock crystal that encloses needlelike crystals of other minerals. Sometimes called Cupid's darts, Venus'-hairstone, or needle stone, sagenite is usually named for the included mineral—thus, tourmalinated quartz, rutilated quartz, etc. Numerous minerals are found included in sagenite, such as actinolite, goethite, epidote, and hornblende, as well as tourmaline and rutile, the latter being the most common. Because some of the needlelike crystals can be seen to cross each other, resulting in a network appearance, the general term sagenite (Greek for net) is used.

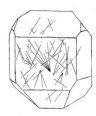

Sagenite is quartz containing closely packed, needlelike crystals. This illustrates a Brazilian specimen.

Quartz Cat's-Eye

Quartz containing inclusions of other minerals so closely packed that there seems to be more of them than of the quartz itself is often spoken of as cat's-eye. This is not the same or as valuable as true cat's-eye of the chrysoberyl variety, and should be called *quartz cat's-eye*. Thin, parallel fibers like asbestos give the polished specimen an opalescent effect. Yellow, green, and brown quartz cat's-eye comes from Germany, India, and Ceylon.

Tiger's-Eye and Hawk's-Eye

When the quartz itself is fibrous, rather than its inclusions, two other attractive varieties are produced. *Tiger's-eye* is a fibrous quartz of a golden brown color, with wavy bands of light which glow and ripple when the gem is rotated. Popular as a cameo stone for men's rings, tiger's-eye is fairly abundant, but comes only from Griqualand West, South Africa. Originally, tiger's-eye was a blue asbestos called crocidolite; after the original coloring matter had been oxidized, the mineral was completely replaced by quartz. When crocidolite is turned into quartz without losing its original blue coloring, the stone is called *hawk's-eye*.

Rose Quartz

Rose quartz is one of the loveliest kinds of quartz. The color varies from pale pink to deep rose. Occurring in irregular masses without crystal faces, rose quartz is difficult to work with, because it breaks into angular pieces with jagged edges, but it can be fashioned into beads, cabochons, and small ornaments. One of the largest deposits of rose quartz in existence is in South Dakota, at the Scott mine near Custer.

Smoky Quartz

A fascinating variety of quartz is *smoky quartz,* with its smoky-yellow to dark-brown—and even black—coloring, which at first glance seems to be opaque, but upon closer examination has a true smoky effect—richly shaded but hazy, and often varying in degree within the same specimen. Smoky quartz is the result of radioactive emanations within the rocks surrounding it, and clear rock crystal can be given a smoky appearance by the use of X-rays and other powerful short-wave rays. Smoky quartz is not widespread, being found chiefly in the Swiss Alps, Spain, and the Pikes Peak region of Colorado. The hazy, light-yellow phase of smoky quartz is so popular in Scotland, where it is called cairngorm, that the deposits there are virtually depleted.

Chalcedony Varieties of Quartz

The chalcedony varieties of quartz are even more varied than the preceding crystalline varieties. They are characteristically translucent or opaque, and occur most frequently as rounded or imitative forms, or as linings in cavities. Many

Ward's Natural Science Establishment

Botryoidal chalcedony from Emery County, Utah, is an interesting form of quartz.

varieties of chalcedony are more familiar by their special names—such as agate, jasper, and onyx—than by the general term, chalcedony. They are popular with engravers because of their abundance, relative hardness, and inexpensiveness, and are cut as cabochons, spheres, transparencies, and novelties.

Carnelian

Red chalcedony—*carnelian*—ranges from pink to blood red, from honey color to orange, depending upon the amount of ferric iron oxide present. It takes a smooth, lustrous polish, making it popular through the centuries for seals and signet stones. While gem-quality carnelian is not abundant, it is available in Brazil and India, and good specimens have been found in Tampa Bay, Florida. When it grades into brown, carnelian is known as sard.

Chrysoprase

The presence of nickel oxide results in apple-green chalcedony—*chrysoprase.* Popular in the time of the Greeks and the Romans, chrysoprase was cut into cameos and intaglios. In Egypt, it was set next to lapis lazuli and also made into beads. It was used lavishly in Europe until the middle of the last century, when the deposits in Silesia were exhausted. With its sudden rarity, it became more expensive and was much imitated. Recent deposits of chrysoprase have been discovered in Oregon and California.

Prase

Prase is a sage-green chalcedony in which the coloring is caused by many green fibers of actinolite included in clear crystalline quartz. Both prase and chrysoprase are used as imitations for jade. The best prase is found in Saxony.

Plasma

Plasma is similar to prase, but is chiefly a fine grass green in color. It is fairly common, being deposited in thick veins or in large masses. The western section of the United States produces plasma in some quantity, and it is also found in North Carolina. The best quality, however, comes from China and India.

Bloodstone

Red and green are found together in *bloodstone,* making a vivid gem stone used for signet rings and sometimes seals and other ornaments. It has been effectively used in carvings representing the Crucifixion. Irregular spots of red, resembling blood, are scattered against the solid dark-green background. Bloodstone is chiefly found in gem quality in India and the Ural Mountains.

Jasper

The deeply colored chalcedonies are termed *jasper.* Because of an excess of coloring matter, jasper is virtually opaque. The presence of iron oxides results in patches or bandings, chiefly red, yellow, brown, and green of differing shades and tints. Ribbon jasper refers to a stone having broad vari-colored stripes. Rounded or angular boulders of jasper are found in conglomerate rocks. Although jasper is fairly common around the world, good specimens have been prized as an ornamental stone. In Russia, art objects have been carved from jasper consisting of red and green stripes.

Moss Agate

Agate and moss agate are probably the best-known kinds of chalcedony. *Moss agate* is particularly popular because of its tiny "landscapes" in stone. These are not actual moss, either plant or fossil, but are intricately branching designs formed by the presence of mineral matter, usually manganese oxide or iron oxide. Chiefly black or brown, but sometimes green, the dendritic patterns form

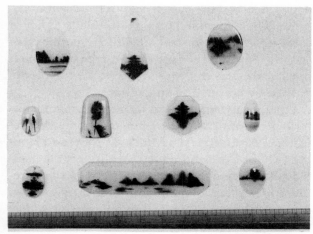

U. S. Geological Survey

"Eternal landscapes in stone" describes the excellent moss agate from Montana. The intricate patterns are not moss or any other living substance.

realistic designs of mountain and forest landscapes against the backdrop of colorless chalcedony. Many beautiful moss agates have come from the gem cutters of India, and in the United States, moss agates can be found in the Western states, particularly Wyoming and Montana.

Agate

Agate is the type of chalcedony in which the colors appear in wavy, concentric bands; these conform to the shape of the cavity in the rock where the silica was originally deposited. As the layers are built up, the size and coloring of the bands varies with the changes in the nature and degree of the impurities being deposited. Innumerable patterns of agate have resulted. The earliest agates were found along the banks of the river Achates (now the Drillo) in Sicily—hence the name. Some of the distinctive varieties of agate include: fortification agate, whose angular bands resemble the outlines of a fort; eye agate, in which complete rings surround a solid center; and iris

agate, which at first appears colorless and then comes to brilliant, rainbow life when held at the proper angle. Because the layers of agate are porous in varying degrees, much experimentation has gone into coloring them chemically—any intensely colorful agate has probably been thus treated.

Onyx

Onyx is chalcedony that is banded in straight, parallel layers of contrasting colors. Alternating layers of black and white or brown and white are the most common, although onyx is often artificially colored. Cameos are usually carved from onyx, the most typical being a white head on a dark field. While true onyx is made up of more than one color, the name sometimes designates solid-black chalcedony. This is now chemically produced with cobalt nitrate and ammonium sulfocyanide, although for centuries it was created by soaking the stone in sugar solution or honey and then charring the sugar with sulfuric acid. Sardonyx is the term used for onyx that includes the color of sard (or the still-redder carnelian) in conjunction with another color, usually white or black.

Petrified Wood

Petrified wood is literally wood turned to stone—frequently gem stone. Trees that have been submerged and preserved from decay are invaded by silica-bearing waters percolating through the ground or rising from heated rock below. The mineral matter is deposited in the cells of the trunks, branches, and even twigs, preserving the original plant structure, sometimes so thoroughly that the exact species of tree can be identified. Many minerals are deposited in petrified wood; silica in the form of chalcedony is the most common. Petrified wood, therefore, is almost always silicified wood. If regular banding is present, it is called agatized wood; brightly colored patches give it the name jasperized wood; and if the silica is in the form of opal, the material is called opalized wood. According to a great number of factors —the kind of trees, state of preservation, coloring matter, and presence of bark—each area of petrified wood has its own characteristics. Excellent forests and smaller areas of petrified wood are found in Patagonia, Canada, and the western United States. Arizona's Petrified Forest National

Monument is the major source of the world's gem-quality silicified wood. There, the trees are scattered over a wide area, with black, blue, reddish-brown, cherry-red, and yellow colors making a most exciting display.

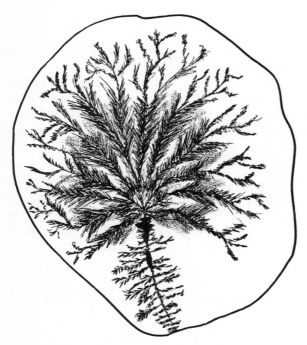

Dendrites are plantlike growths of crystalline origin. Most are composed of manganese oxide. These are on Texas limestone.

Chert and Flint

Two other types of chalcedony quartz are *chert* and *flint.* They resemble each other, but chert is white or light gray, whereas flint is gray, smoky brown, or brownish black. Because flint has a conchoidal fracture, it was much used by primitive man in the fashioning of arrowheads, knives, and hatchets. It was employed in striking sparks to start a fire.

Opal

Opal, which is the noncrystalline hydrous silica, is deposited as a jelly from hot springs, hardening as it cools. This cooling results in cracks, which may be filled with other opal material, so that layers are built up within the stone, reflecting light rays in the same way as do soap bubbles. Depending upon the layers and the direction from which they are viewed, certain colors result—and every

color is present in its purest hue. Opal is delicate, being somewhat brittle and subject to disintegration from loss of water or excessive heat.

White opal (or Hungarian opal) was the precious opal of ancient times, having a brilliant scintillation against a solid, light background. Black opal has a dark background, usually blue or gray, and is at present exceedingly scarce. Fire opal, being the only variety that is transparent, may be faceted. It has a yellow, orange, or red body color, and the play of color is deep within the stone. The many kinds of opal that lack a play of color are called common opal and resemble chalcedony. Perhaps the best-known type of common opal is siliceous sinter (or geyserite) which is deposited by hot springs and geysers.

Opal is surrounded by a long and romantic history. Precious opal has been mined in Central Europe, Australia, Asia Minor, Mexico, and Honduras. Not least of the opal localities is northern Nevada, although the specimens from there frequently develop a series of fine cracks upon exposure to the atmosphere. Common opal is widely distributed.

Quartz Rocks

While not all sand is composed of quartz, typical sand consists of quartz grains of more or less uniform size, resulting from the breakdown of some pre-existing rocks. If the grains are angular and sharp-edged, it is probable that the sand lies near where it was originally formed; sand that has been transported by wind, running water, or the waves of the sea is made up of grains that have been worn rounded and smooth. Much commercial use is made of sand—in the manufacture of glass and cement, for grinding and polishing, in the molding of metal castings, for sand blasting, and many other uses. Gravel, which is made up of much coarser fragments, is used as ballast for railroads and in highway construction, because it packs well and is resistant to wear.

Conglomerate

Conglomerate results when gravel and sand have been cemented together into firm rock by percolating, mineral-laden water. Depending upon the types of pebbles incorporated in it, a conglomerate is called gneiss-conglomerate, quartz-conglomerate, etc. Some quartz conglomerate is cut and polished to make building stone.

Sandstone

Sandstone ranges widely in composition, firmness, and texture, for it is a sedimentary rock made up of medium-sized fragments of older rocks and minerals cemented together by a great variety of bonding substances: silica, iron oxide, and calcium carbonate, for example. Sometimes, when the sandstone has been formed chiefly by compaction under great pressure, there is very little cementing material present. Such a sandstone, although consisting almost entirely of well-rounded quartz grains, is not at all strong. Most sandstones are quite porous, some having a porosity as high as 25 percent. It is this feature that makes the rock such an effective storehouse of petroleum and natural gas, which move through its open spaces.

Because sandstone is usually a bedded rock, easy to quarry, it has always been popular as an exterior and interior building stone, for paving and flagging, and for industrial uses such as grindstones. Depending upon the cementing substance present, sandstone has been given a great variety of names. Siliceous sandstone, usually the hardest, is cemented with silica; calcareous sandstone, being cemented with lime, is usually fairly soft. Sandstone cemented with any of the iron oxides is termed ferruginous, while sandstone held together with clay impurities is called argillaceous. Other types are named according to their composition: arkose, such as the famous Old Red Sandstone of the British Isles, is made up of quartz and a fairly large amount of feldspar. A special, curious type of sandstone is itacolumite—"the rock that bends." This sandstone, found in India and North Carolina and associated with diamonds in Brazil, is actually flexible and will sag under its own weight or bend in opposite directions under pressure. The flexibility is due, apparently, to the presence of talc and mica and other such soft, layered minerals, as

well as to the symmetrical arrangement of the quartz grains.

Quartzite

Quartzite, being a metamorphosed sandstone, is an extremely hard rock with a glistening appearance caused by its crystalline structure. While sandstone breaks around the individual grains, quartzite fractures as easily through them as through the cement. This is because quartzite is so solidly unified by heat, pressure, and the silica that cements the grains. Quartzite is white when pure, but most of it contains mica, iron, feldspar, or other mineral particles that alter the color to gray, brown, red, or even yellow, green, or black. Owing to its extreme hardness, quartzite does not have

No two agates are alike. Brazil, the source of this one, is world famous for the quality and number of its agates.

many commercial uses except for road ballast and in concrete work. Because it is so durable, it will be found in areas where intensive mountain-making activity has occurred, protecting hills and ridges from the erosion that has weathered away the less durable features of the topography.

Petrified wood frequently shows bark turned to stone along with the rest of the material. Sweetwater County, Wyoming, furnished this specimen.

U. S. Geological Survey

Denver Convention and Tourist Bureau

The largest petrified tree stump yet discovered stands near Florissant, Colorado. It is more than fifty feet around.

Chapter 11

THE MINERAL RESOURCES OF FIFTY STATES

Chapter 11

THE MINERAL RESOURCES OF FIFTY STATES

Look for uranium where uranium has been found is advice well taken. It applies equally to gold or to gems, or to minerals in general, and it recognizes the preference of most persons to be on the side of favorable odds. It does not, however, take into account the initial discoveries of the pioneer, and the ever-possible chance of your making an original find in virgin territory and of opening up a new field in an unexpected place. Even with the strongest desire for complete freedom to search where he wants, the prospector or collector would nevertheless be daring—indeed, perhaps merely foolish—to ignore entirely the results of earlier mineral recoveries in any except new and unexplored land. Copper is more likely to be found in Arizona than in most other states, and gem stones perhaps in California or Colorado—statements supported by common sense and production statistics, if nothing else. The mineral hunter should always, of course, pay close attention to the rock types and mineral associations that have proved favorable in the past.

In order to encourage the further investigation of America's mineral wealth, the principal mineral resources of each of the fifty states are summarized in this chapter, giving information not readily obtainable in other books on this subject.

Although among our most important natural substances, coal is not the usual object of the prospector's efforts; then, too, petroleum discoveries are left to the experienced judgment and elaborate equipment of the professional geologist. In all the rest—whether ores of metals to make a rocket, exotic fuels to propel it to the moon, ordinary but very useful rocks for construction materials to build the nation, or colorful gems to adorn its people—the opportunities are wide open.

Alabama

Alabama ranks second among the states producing bauxite (the sole ore of aluminum) and third as a producer of iron ore, in the form of hematite and limonite. Prominent also in the mineral industry of this state are coal and petroleum resources. Alabama has a plentiful supply of sand and gravel, and of clay, which are used commercially.

Alaska

The 1896 gold rush to the Klondike first made this state famous for its mineral wealth. Gold is still important in Alaska, but many other minerals are of increasing significance today. The only tin mines in North America are located on the Seward Peninsula. Other mineral products include silver, copper, platinum, mercury, tungsten, antimony, chromite, barite, graphite, gypsum, and sulfur. Gem stones found in Alaska include agate, petrified wood, and especially nephrite jade. While no deposits of uranium have yet been mined, prospectors continue their search for it, and there are good reasons to hope for its discovery. Alaska will someday be one of the world's great sources of petroleum.

Arizona

Copper is the chief mineral product of Arizona; about one-half of the nation's total output now comes from this one state. Mining is, indeed, Arizona's biggest industry. Other ores found in good supply include gold and silver, lead and zinc, manganese, vanadium, molybdenum, tungsten, and uranium. Mercury and beryl have been found in modest quantities. Among the nonmetallic mineral resources of Arizona are limestone for the cement industry, clay, asbestos, barite, feldspar, fluorspar, perlite, pumice, building stone, and sand and gravel. A variety of gem stones are found, especially turquoise, and also amethyst, agate, petrified wood, jasper, and other varieties of chalcedony.

Arkansas

The only diamond mine in North America is found in Arkansas, but it seems too lean to be worked on a commercial scale. Instead, it is operated as a tourist attraction. The rock crystal from Hot Springs is splendid, and the Magnet Cove area is a remarkable collecting ground. Two-thirds of the state's mineral production, however, comes from its stores of petroleum, natural gas, and coal. Arkansas supplies most of America's domestic bauxite for aluminum. Other mineral substances in good amount include barite, manganese, gypsum, limestone, slate, sand and gravel, and stone.

California

Brought into the Union by the gold rush of 1848, California now ranks fourth among the states in gold production. Platinum and silver, lead and zinc, mercury, tungsten, molybdenum, chromite, manganese, iron ore, the boron minerals, and the rare-earth metals are also found in California. Gypsum, sand and gravel, and clay are plentiful. California's gem tourmaline, jade, and kunzite are outstanding. The Crestmore quarry is exceptional among the world's famed mineral localities.

Colorado

Since the gold rush of 1859, with its rallying cry of "Pikes Peak or Bust," Colorado has been an important mineral-producing state. Gold, silver, copper, lead, and zinc have all played their part in Colorado history. Climax produces more of the world's molybdenum than any other place, together with its by-products of tungsten, pyrite, and tin. The future development of oil shale has

been much in the news. There is a substantial industrial use made of rock for cement, as well as of sand and gravel, and clay. Fluorspar, feldspar, perlite, and gypsum are abundant. Among the gem stones are turquoise, agate, amazonstone, aquamarine, topaz, and smoky quartz. Uranium and its associate, vanadium, are found in Colorado; deposits on the Colorado Plateau, extending into adjacent states, are among the most prolific known.

Connecticut

Mineral production in Connecticut is confined mainly to the nonmetallic minerals. Sand and gravel and stone predominate, and mica is mined for industrial use. Feldspar is used in the pottery and porcelain industries.

Delaware

Delaware's chief mineral products are sand and gravel, stone, and clay, which are used in the building industries and as aggregate and road material.

Florida

Clay, limestone, and phosphate rock are the primary industrial minerals of Florida. The phosphate workings are immense. Titanium in the form of ilmenite and rutile in heavy-sand deposits has come into prominence. Zircon occurs in the same Florida sands.

Georgia

Of Georgia's mineral output, 98 percent is accounted for by the nonmetallics. Clay—especially kaolin and china clay—is the largest single mineral product in the state. Limestone and slate are abundant; the excellent marble and granite are widely known. Asbestos, barite, mica, and talc are mined in quantity, and manganese, iron ore, and bauxite are also extracted. Phosphate rock, gold, and miscellaneous gem stones are found in lesser amounts. Georgia once led the country in the production of gold.

Hawaii

Because Hawaii is volcanic in origin and tropical in climate, its mineral resources consist primarily of coral sand, volcanic ash, crushed lava rock, clay, and limestone. Although iron ore, bauxite, nickel, chromium, titanium, and magnesium occur in the lava rocks, they have not yet been developed commercially.

Idaho

Like most other Western states, Idaho has a history of gold and silver booms. Today, lead, silver, and zinc are the most important mineral products of the state. Other mineral resources in Idaho include ores of copper, cobalt, tungsten, and the rare-earth metals, as well as cement and phosphate rock, sand and gravel, building stone, clay, barite, gypsum, pumice, and abrasive garnet. Thorium, ilmenite, magnetite, and zircon are among the newer mineral substances to be produced commercially.

Illinois

Illinois ranks fourth in the United States in coal mining, and has abundant supplies of petroleum, natural gas, and peat. Sand and gravel, clay, building stone, limestone, and fluorspar are among other valuable mineral materials in this state.

Indiana

Over 80 percent of all the building limestone used in the United States comes from Indiana. The famous Bedford limestone has been used for construction in virtually every city in the nation. The state's other chief mineral products are also in the industrial, nonmetallic field, and include gypsum, limestone for cement, and sand and gravel.

Iowa

Cement, sand and gravel, building stone, clay, gypsum, and peat are the most important mineral products in Iowa. Cement from limestone and sand and gravel are the most important industrially, while gypsum is being given increased attention.

Kansas

Petroleum production is high in Kansas, this state ranking fifth in the United States. Natural gas and helium are other important mineral products, with large reserves available. Limestone and sand and gravel are also abundant. Vast beds of salt underlie parts of Kansas. Characteristic of the southeastern corner, in the Tri-State district, are zinc and lead deposits.

Kentucky

Considerable commercial use is made in Kentucky of fluorspar, sand and gravel, stone, clay, and limestone for cement. Natural gas and natural gasoline are prominent among the mineral fuels.

Louisiana

The greater part of Louisiana's mineral riches comes from deep wells sunk into the earth for petroleum, natural gas, salt, and sulfur. These are largely associated with the remarkable "salt domes" that follow the shoreline of the Gulf of Mexico. Other abundant mineral products include limestone, sand and gravel, clay, and cement rock.

Maine

This state possesses a variety of mineral resources: feldspar, beryllium, mica, limestone, slate, granite, and some metallic ores. Maine is a source for tourmaline, beryl, and apatite—gem minerals for which it has long been known.

Maryland

Mineral production in Maryland is primarily concerned with coal, natural gas, clay, limestone, sand, and gravel. Minor amounts of other minerals—such as mica, beryl, talc, soapstone, slate, marble, and limestone—are also found in the state.

Massachusetts

Massachusetts' mineral output emphasizes stone, sand and gravel, clay, and limestone. Of the stone quarries in the state, the majority have produced granite. Basalt, limestone, and sandstone have also been quarried, although more so in past years than now.

Michigan

That part of the Lake Superior belt of iron ore that lies in Michigan produces 8 percent of the nation's iron. The country's largest cement mill is located at Alpena. Michigan far exceeds any other state in the production of peat, and ranks second in sand and gravel, as well as magnesium compounds. It is first in the production of salt, which comes from the thickest beds in America. Gypsum and clay are also abundant.

Minnesota

Nearly 70 percent of the country's iron ore comes from Minnesota, where it is obtained primarily by open-pit mining. Maganese-bearing iron ore is also present. Limestone, clay, sand and gravel, granite for building stone, and peat are other prominent industrial minerals and rocks produced in Minnesota. Especially fascinating are the historic quarries at Pipestone National Monument, from which the Plains Indians for untold centuries extracted the red pipestone for their peace pipes.

Mississippi

Fuels, mainly petroleum, make up 90 percent of Mississippi's mineral production. Industrially, sand and gravel, cement rock and other stone, and clay lead the state's mineral resources. Mississippi also produces bentonite and bauxite.

Missouri

Missouri ranks first in this country in the production of lead and barite, and third in fire clay. Cement, construction stone, and sand and gravel are also produced in abundance. Other minerals in the state include ores of copper, zinc, and silver, and some of iron.

Montana

Montana has truly earned the name "Treasure State." The minerals found in Montana are both plentiful and varied. Its motto, *Oro y Plata* (Gold and Silver), suggests its mineral wealth, but Montana is most often thought of in terms of copper. Lead and zinc are also mined in quantity. Coal is plentiful, as are oil and natural gas. Cement, asbestos, and phosphoric acid are produced, and the state ranks first in the production of vermiculite. Other mineral deposits include fluorspar and gypsum, and ores of manganese, chromium, and tungsten.

Nebraska

Crude petroleum accounts for 50 percent of Ne-

braska's mineral production, with natural gas and related liquids close behind. Other mineral resources of importance in the state include limestone for cement, stone, sand and gravel, clay, and pumicite.

Nevada

While Nevada is nicknamed the "Silver State" and is famous for Virginia City and the Comstock Lode, its principal mineral production today is that of copper, zinc, gold, and tungsten. In fact, over 80 percent of Nevada's mineral production is in metals: lead, mercury, iron, and manganese, in addition to those already mentioned. Low-grade uranium has been found in the state, and prospectors are searching for more and richer deposits. Beryllium-bearing minerals are a recent discovery. The nonmetallic mineral substances include diatomite, barite, fluorspar, limestone, gypsum, pumice, clay, talc, and soapstone.

New Hampshire

New Hampshire granite is deservedly famous, and the state also has a well-developed production of sand and gravel, stone, and clay products. Other mineral resources include feldspar, mica, beryl, abrasive garnet, abrasive quartz-mica schist, and ores of copper, lead, iron, and columbium-tantalum. There is also a little gold.

New Jersey

A variety of mineral products are found in New Jersey—iron and zinc ore, limestone, sulfur, peat, clay, and sand and gravel. The zinc mines at Ogdensburg are a noteworthy source of spectacular fluorescent specimens. The stone quarried in the state includes basalt, granite, marble, and limestone.

New Mexico

Petroleum, natural gas, natural-gas liquids, and potassium salts account for over 80 percent of the mineral production of New Mexico. This state mines close to 90 percent of the potash used in the United States. Other mineral resources include copper, lead, zinc, gold, mica, tungsten, gypsum, and pumice. The nation's largest reserves of uranium ore have been proved to exist in northeastern New Mexico, and development is increasing yearly.

New York

The processing of salt is one of the major mineral industries of New York. Other resources include cement rock, sand and gravel, clay, slate, and stone—chiefly limestone, marble, and basalt. Iron ore, zinc, and some lead and silver are produced, and gypsum and abrasive garnet are two other valuable mineral substances found here. Black tourmaline and clear quartz are among the choice collectors' specimens obtained.

North Carolina

More than 300 minerals and rocks, including many gems, are found in North Carolina, and seventy of these are of some commercial importance. Over 50 percent of North Carolina's mineral production comes, however, from sand, gravel, and stone. Abrasives, clay, mica, and concentrates of beryllium and tungsten are also important, and the state possesses gold, silver, copper, and lead deposits. Much of the American output of kaolin comes from North Carolina.

North Dakota

The state's primary mineral products are coal, petroleum, natural gas, clay, and sand and gravel. North Dakota has more than 75 percent of the nation's reserves of lignite.

Ohio

Ohio is the leading producer of grindstones, clay, and limestone for cement, and it ranks third in sand and gravel. Stone, coal, and peat are also abundant mineral products of the state, and salt is another important commodity. The celestite and fluorite from Clay Center make very desirable specimen material.

Oklahoma

Oklahoma's history is written in its oil wells. Its income is based on petroleum and natural gas, and oil derricks stand in front of the state capitol in Oklahoma City. In addition, its native asphalt makes up the country's largest reserve. Lead, zinc, and gypsum are important mineral products, and

the state possesses extensive deposits of clay. Crushed limestone, granite blocks, sawed limestone, and sandstone are also important.

Oregon

Oregon's chief mineral output lies in the nonmetallic field: limestone for cement, clay, shale, and stone—especially basalt from the scenic Columbia River lava flows. Gold, silver, copper, and lead are found in minor quantities, as are mercury and nickel. There has been a recent increase in the production of zirconium and hafnium. Agates are cut in quantity as gem stones.

Pennsylvania

Pennsylvania produces a wide variety of minerals. Over 75 percent of its mineral production is in fuels, primarily its superb anthracite and bituminous coal, but the state is also a source of iron ore, limestone, and slate. Sandstone, granite, and basalt are available in commercial quantities, as well as a variety of other rocks, such as serpentine, gneiss, and mica schist.

Rhode Island

Limestone, granite, basalt, and graphite are the mineral products here. The coal beds have been so highly altered by ancient mountain-making that much of the coal has turned to graphite.

South Carolina

While clay, sand and gravel, and stone make up the major portion of South Carolina's mineral production, barite and mica, phosphate rock, manganese, and gold are also found there. More recently, deposits of monazite have been developed.

South Dakota

South Dakota leads in the production of gold in the United States. The largest gold mine in the country is the Homestake, situated at Lead. Clay, sand and gravel, and stone—chiefly limestone and granite—are also available in quantity. Other mineral products include feldspar and mica, beryl, columbium-tantalum, lithium, and bentonite. South Dakota contains the most easterly large-scale deposits of uranium in the country. Gem stones include the finest of rose quartz, agate and agatized wood, and garnet.

Tennessee

Of the Southern states, Tennessee has the greatest variety of minerals. There is a good deal of industrial use of cement, ferroalloys, clay, phosphate rock, attractive marble, and limestone. Iron ore is produced, as are manganese and much zinc. There is also some copper, gold, and silver.

Texas

Texas is noted for its oil production. It also accounts for about 75 percent of the country's sulfur. Natural gas, helium, and salt are available in quantity. Magnesium is extracted from the sea. Cement, clay, stone, sand and gravel, gypsum, lime, iron ore, and some silver are also produced. Among the gem stones native to Texas are agate, agatized wood, jasper, fine blue topaz, rock crystal, opal, amethyst, and labradorite.

Utah

Utah stands second in the nation in the production of copper, molybdenum, and gold. It is the only commercial source of gilsonite, a curious natural hydrocarbon. Ores of lead, zinc, silver, iron, manganese, and tungsten, and potash, phosphate rock, limestone for cement, clay, and salt are also found in this state. Marble and some gem stones occur in Utah, also, and there is important production of uranium and vanadium.

Vermont

Stone quarrying always comes to mind when one thinks of Vermont. This most important mineral industry in the state thrives on great quantities of granite, marble, and limestone. Slate, asbestos, and talc are also produced, and there are some deposits of gold, silver, and copper.

Virginia

Stone, sand and gravel, and zinc are the leading mineral products of Virginia, which also possesses an unusual variety of other mineral resources. These include lead, manganese, beryl, clay, slate, titanium, silver, gypsum, kyanite, mica, salt, and such stones as serpentine, granite quartzite, marble, and limestone.

Washington

A good many minerals are found in Washington. In the order of their commercial value, they include cement rock, coal, sand and gravel, and stone (limestone and basalt, primarily). Other mineral products available in varying quantities are gold and silver, lead and zinc, mercury and tungsten ores, platinum, magnesite, and silica and silicified wood. Exploration and prospecting for uranium has become important since the autunite discoveries on the Spokane Indian Reservation.

West Virginia

Mineral resources in West Virginia mean mostly high-quality coal. Clay, limestone, sulfur, cement, sand and gravel, and raw stone are also prominent mineral products in the state. Salt is available, and silica sand is used in the state's glass- and bottle-making industry.

Wisconsin

Mineral resources in Wisconsin are primarily nonmetallic: cement rock, sand and gravel, clay, and stone—granite, limestone, sandstone, and basalt. Iron, zinc, and lead are also produced; although less well known than similar deposits in other states, they are of both economic and historic interest.

Wyoming

The mineral resources of Wyoming are not fully developed, but they hold a magnificent potential. The prospects for petroleum development are substantial. Wyoming is one of the principal producers of gem stones, including jade, agate, and petrified wood. The mining of iron and uranium shows great promise. This state is the foremost producer of bentonite. It ranks first in the nation in the production of trona (hydrous sodium carbonate). Wyoming still offers a frontier to the mineral seeker.

Chapter 12

MINERAL PUBLICATIONS

Chapter 12

MINERAL PUBLICATIONS

Between the covers of a good mineral publication—whether newspaper, magazine, or book—may be found a variety of useful information for the prospector and mineral collector.

Each issue of these periodicals contains much of value to increase one's knowledge of the rapidly moving events in the world of minerals, including: news of latest mineral discoveries and current production; new uses for earth substances long known; improved methods of prospecting and mining. There are also editorial discussions of pertinent problems. Illustrated articles and stories about mineral localities, often accompanied by good route maps, are of great interest, especially during the long winter months when the mineral hunter will be planning his trips for the seasons following. Letters will put you in touch with collectors who may wish to exchange specimens. These periodicals tell of available literature, much of which is free; of new museum acquisitions worth seeing; and of coming mineral and mining shows, exhibits, and conventions. Their photographs are sources of pictures for school work and scrapbooks. Not of least usefulness are the many advertisements of dealers offering specimens and equipment of all kinds.

Many good books are available on the subject of minerals and rocks. Your book dealer and librarian can be of aid in selecting those that suit your particular needs. Standard and well-recommended books on general prospecting, uranium prospecting, and mineral collecting are described in this chapter.

Magazines

The following magazines are edited on a popular level and have a national distribution. In addition, a large number of trade and technical journals may be consulted in public libraries.

Gems and Minerals. Edited by Don MacLachlan and published monthly at Box 687, Mentone, California. Price $3.00 per year; sample copy 35 cents.

Rocks and Minerals. Edited by Peter Zodac and published bimonthly at Box 29, Peekskill, New York. Price $3.00 per year; sample copy 60 cents.

The Mineralogist. Edited by Don MacLachlan and published bimonthly at Box 808, Mentone, California. Price $2.00 per year; sample copy 35 cents.

Earth Science. Edited by Dr. Ben Hur Wilson and published bimonthly at Box 1357, Chicago 90, Illinois. Price $2.50 per year; sample copy 45 cents.

The Lapidary Journal. Edited by Hugh Leiper and published bimonthly at Box 518, Del Mar, California. Price $3.00 per year; sample copy 50 cents.

Desert. Published by Charles E. Shelton monthly at Palm Desert, California. Price $4.00 per year; sample copy 40 cents.

Uranium Prospector and American Outdoorsman. Edited by Wayne Winters and published monthly at Box 987, Cedar Rapids, Iowa. Price $1.50 per year; sample copy 15 cents.

Books

General Prospecting

Handbook for Prospectors and Operators of Small Mines, by Max W. Von Bernewitz; 4th edition revised by Harry C. Chellson and published in 1943 by the McGraw-Hill Book Company, Inc., New York. An extensive treatise on the techniques of prospecting and the equipment used.

Prospecting and Operating Small Gold Placers, by William F. Boericke; 2d edition published in 1936 by John Wiley and Sons, Inc., New York. A rather short but very useful book.

Alluvial Prospecting and Mining, by S. V. Griffith; 2d edition published in 1960 by Pergamon Press, Inc., New York. Exploration, prospecting, and exploitation of placer deposits.

Prospecting for Gold and Silver, by Eros M. Savage; published in 1934 by the McGraw-Hill Book Company, Inc., New York. A practical guide.

Popular Prospecting, by H. C. Dake; published in 1955 and distributed by *Gems and Minerals,* Mentone, Calif. An elementary guide.

Uranium Prospecting

Minerals for Atomic Energy, by Robert D. Nininger; 2d edition published in 1956 by D. Van Nostrand Company, Inc., New York. The most comprehensive coverage of uranium, thorium, and beryllium minerals and deposits, from exploration to sale.

The following three books are on an intermediate level and are all excellent:

The Uranium Prospector's Guide, by Thomas J. Ballard and Quentin E. Conklin; published in 1955 by Harper & Brothers, New York.

Prospecting for Atomic Minerals, by Alvin W. Knoerr and George P. Lutjen; published in 1955 by the McGraw-Hill Book Company, Inc., New York.

Uranium. Where It Is and How to Find It, by Paul Dean Proctor, Edmond P. Hyatt, and Kenneth C. Bullock; published in 1954 by Eagle Rock Publications, Salt Lake City, Utah.

The following three books are small but worthwhile publications obtainable from the U. S. Government Printing Office, Washington 25, D.C.:

Prospecting for Uranium; published in 1957 by the U. S. Atomic Energy Commission and the U. S. Geological Survey (75 cents).

Prospecting with a Counter, by Robert J. Wright; published in 1954 by the U. S. Atomic Energy Commission (30 cents).

Facts Concerning Uranium Exploration and Production, by John E. Crawford and James Paone; published in 1956 by the U. S. Bureau of Mines (70 cents).

Mineral Collecting

How to Know the Minerals and Rocks, by Richard M. Pearl; published in 1955 by the McGraw-Hill Book Company, Inc., New York, and in a Signet Key edition by the New American Library of World Literature, Inc., New York. A practical field guide to more than 125 important minerals and rocks, featuring basic keys for identifying typical specimens without special skill or equipment; includes many marked drawings and color plates.

1001 Questions Answered about the Mineral Kingdom, by Richard M. Pearl; published in 1959 by Dodd, Mead and Company, New York. Full answers to the questions most often asked about major branches of the mineral kingdom.

Getting Acquainted with Minerals, by George Letchworth English and David E. Jensen; 2d edition published in 1958 by the McGraw-Hill Book Company, Inc., New York. An introductory, well-illustrated book on mineral properties, descriptions of minerals, and information for collectors.

Rocks and Minerals, by Richard M. Pearl; published in 1956 by Barnes & Noble, Inc., New York. A survey of minerals and rocks in everyday language, covering all aspects of most interest; contains color plates.

Quartz Family Minerals, by Henry C. Dake, Frank L. Fleener, and Ben Hur Wilson; published in 1938 by the McGraw-Hill Book Company, Inc., New York. A complete book about quartz for the collector; well illustrated.

How to Collect Minerals, by Peter Zodac; published in 1934 by *Rocks and Minerals,* Peekskill, New York. An elementary book about many phases of collecting minerals and rocks, especially for the beginner.

Popular Gemology, by Richard M. Pearl; 2d edition published in 1958 by Sage Books, Denver,

Colorado. A modern, finely illustrated standard book about gems, written in layman's language.

Ultraviolet Guide to Minerals, by Sterling Gleason; published in 1960 by D. Van Nostrand Company, Inc., New York. A new book on prospecting for, and collecting, fluorescent minerals.

Locality guides like those named below are being published for many states and regions; the magazines mentioned previously carry notices, reviews, and advertisements of them.

Gem Hunter's Guide, by Russell P. MacFall; 2d edition published in 1958 by Science and Mechanics Publishing Company, Chicago. A useful book which includes a listing of mineral localities in the United States.

Colorado Gem Trails and Mineral Guide, by Richard M. Pearl; published in 1958 by Sage Books, Denver, Colorado. A detailed locality guide, with maps and road logs.

Mineralogical Journeys in Arizona, by Arthur L. Flagg; published in 1958 by Bitner's, Scottsdale, Arizona. A thorough treatment of mineral discoveries in Arizona.

INDEX

INDEX